*Computer Applications
in Architecture
and Engineering*

Computer Applications
in Architecture
and Engineering

G. NEIL HARPER
Editor

New York   San Francisco

Toronto   London   Sydney

McGRAW-HILL BOOK COMPANY

Contributors

Charles F. Beck
Sargent & Lundy Engineers
Chicago, Illinois

G. Neil Harper
Skidmore, Owings & Merrill
Chicago, Illinois

Richard I. Krauss, AIA
Ashley, Myer and Associates, Inc.
Cambridge, Massachusetts

Richard C. La Velle
Arthur Andersen & Co.
Chicago, Illinois

William Hines Linder
University of South Carolina
Columbia, South Carolina

Theodore H. Myer
Bolt, Beranek and Newman, Inc.
Cambridge, Massachusetts

Lavette C. Teague, Jr., AIA
Massachusetts Institute of Technology
Cambridge, Massachusetts

Charles B. Thomsen, AIA
Caudill Rowlett Scott
New York, New York

Preface

This book addresses itself to the application of computer techniques in professional practice. The material and scope are directed primarily to the practicing architect and engineer. The overall emphasis of the book is one of practical applications for a professional office; and applications are discussed from selected topics in engineering, architectural production, accounting, specifications, etc. Hence a rather broad band of office problems is sketched out in varying detail but with enough examples to demonstrate the feasibility of computer application.

No mathematical ability other than the ability to count and to reason is required of the reader. The book is not intended to present the interesting yet intricate mathematics behind some of the more sophisticated applications. Neither does the book serve as a primer for those who want to learn to program a computer. Instead, the essential emphasis of the book has been chosen with the idea in mind of the architect or engineer who wishes to see what applications of the computer are currently being made in the architectural-engineering profession.

A volume of this sort must be very humble in its claim either to completeness or to a compelling *raison d'être*. On the one hand, it is obvious that no single volume is likely to cover every important application of computers in the broad fields of architecture and engineering. On the other hand, there may be some question as to whether or not there is even a sufficient number of applications within the limited scope of architectural-engineering office practice to warrant a complete book on the subject. The only answer to both these positions is that many architects and engineers throughout the nation seem to have an inherent curiosity concerning computer applications. This volume is an initial attempt to satisfy that curiosity.

G. Neil Harper

Contents

SEVEN   *Computer-based Management Techniques for the Architectural-Engineering Office*
William H. Linder

EIGHT   *Architecture and the Computer*
Charles B. Thomsen

NINE   *Research in Computer Applications to Architecture*
Lavette C. Teague, Jr.

TEN   *Coming Attractions*
G. Neil Harper

Computer Applications
in Architecture
and Engineering

CHAPTER ONE *Computer Fundamentals*

By G. Neil Harper

Beginning with a projection of the magnitude of the computer-age revolution in which we are now living, these initial pages introduce, in lay terms, the important concepts of computer technology. Brief discussions of the basic nature and essential hardware components of a computer are followed by the notion of the progression in software from machine languages to problem-oriented languages. Examples of these languages are given in an attempt to illustrate some of the computer fundamentals which eventually are at the root of every application problem.

Dr. Harper is an Associate Partner at Skidmore, Owings and Merrill, Chicago, Illinois. He holds a B.S. in Civil Engineering from M.I.T., 1959, and an M.S., 1961, and a Ph.D., 1963 from the University of Illinois in Urbana. He has done postdoctoral work in Hanover, Germany, and Delft, Holland, in shell mechanics and has taught at the University of Illinois and at Northwestern University. Dr. Harper is a Research Affiliate of M.I.T. and a Visiting Lecturer at the University of Illinois, Chicago. His responsibilities at Skidmore, Owings and Merrill include both project engineering and supervision of computer activities throughout the firm.

1.1   Introduction

The remarkable force with which the computer is entering our society in nearly all its aspects can be aptly illustrated by the following observation: Whenever technology produces a tool that provides a change in the *order of magnitude* of a previous ability, a profound change in society will be in the offing in a more or less rapid fashion. For example, the invention of the rudimentary wheel enabled man to carry at least ten times as much in the first crude cart as he had been able to carry on his back. This may well have been one of the first technological inventions of man, and as such it set in motion a basic pattern of change in society that continues to the present day.

Numerous other examples in relatively recent technological history could also be cited to reinforce the notion that a change of an order of magnitude in man's capabilities, i.e., an increase by a factor of 10, 100, 1000, . . . etc., inevitably produces a profound change in society as a whole. The invention of the microscope, which enables man to observe particles many hundreds or even thousands of times smaller than what he can see with the unaided human eye, has been instrumental in raising medical practice from medieval witchcraft to the modern science of healing that touches so much of humanity today. The invention of the telescope, which extends man's vision by several orders of magnitude far out into the universe, not only has changed man's conception of our place in the universe from Ptolemaic to Copernican (with all the scientific and philosophic implications of that change) but has also given rise to the modern science of astronomy—without whose accurate observations and calculations our current feats in space would be completely impossible. The invention of the steam engine multiplied man's muscle by a factor of ten—a simple change of one order of magnitude. The basic change in our society following this development—a change the historians call the Industrial Revolution—has been unique in man's history. Countless other examples could be added from modern technologies which are just beginning to have an effect on society—atomic fission, the transistor, and the laser are just a few of the tremendously important advances that are now impinging on our technological frontiers.

In an attempt to gain some appreciation of the severity of the jolt that the digital computer has given society, consider this last sequence of very common examples of the way that an increase in orders of magnitude has changed man's modus operandi. Man walks at about 4 miles per hour. The automobile enables him to travel one order of magnitude faster—say 40 miles per hour. The major effects of automobiles, in terms of convenience, mobility, congestion, air pollution and traffic fatalities are abundantly clear to even the most casual observer. Introduction of the airplane, particularly jet-powered craft, enabled man to travel about an order of magnitude faster than the automobile. The extreme mobility characteristic of American life in the last ten years, and indeed the concept of a "shrinking world," have been a direct result of this change in the order of magnitude of our speed of travel.

Consider now that man can make elementary decisions or do simple arithmetic in one or two seconds. Modern digital computers can do the same operations in roughly one one-millionth of a second—a change in order of magnitude not of one or two, as in the case of the automobile or airplane, but of *six*. From this perspective, one gains a basic philosophic appreciation of the magnitude of the change that the digital computer has brought and will continue to bring to our way of life. Just as the Industrial Revolution and its sequel of developments extended man's muscle, the current Computer Revolution is extending man's mind.

From the wealth of computer effects already evident around us, it is astounding to recall that the first commercial computer was installed in the early fifties—barely fifteen years ago. Extrapolation into the future from such a short time base is simultaneously both an exciting temptation and an invitation to error. Although the final chapter of the book does contain a few projections into the future for developments that may have major impact on architectural and engineering education and practice, the intervening chapters concentrate on practical computer applications of the present and short-term future in the professional office.

The remaining portion of this first chapter is devoted to a presentation, in layman's terms, of some elementary computer fundamentals. The aim of such a presentation is to dispel the mystery that sometimes surrounds modern computers and thereby to persuade the reader that the computer is simply a tool which he can and should use effectively in pursuit of his profession.

1.2   The Binary Nature of Nature

In a host of fascinating varieties, our world is composed of binary elements. By binary is meant, of course, the choice between two and only two stable states—either yes-no, left-right, on-off, etc. Mankind is divided biologically into male or female, time can be divided into alternate sequences of day and night, and space in the trunk of the family automobile either is or is not sufficient to hold the baggage for the planned vacation. In other words, much of nature is binary.

When one reflects on this basic premise, it is really not surprising to find that digital computers are also essentially binary in composition. One notes that holes are either punched or not punched in paper cards, electric current is either flowing or not flowing, a switch is either open or closed, magnetization is either north or south, present or not present, clockwise or counterclockwise. The question of whether the nature of the computer is male or female is left for the reader as a homework exercise.

As a direct consequence of the binary nature of modern electronics, computers function internally with a binary number system. Fortunately or unfortunately, depending on one's point of view, man functions internally with a decimal number system—probably because he has evolved with ten fingers and ten toes. Had man evolved with only two fingers and two toes, communication with modern computers would no doubt be a good deal simpler. Within the foreseeable future of the next few million years, it appears unlikely that this basic division between man and machine will change. Hence it is necessary to consider the essential characteristics of two number systems: decimal and binary.

In order to understand the binary number system of the computer more easily, and how one translates from binary to decimal or decimal to binary, let us investigate first the more familiar decimal number system. In particular, let us investigate what is meant by a decimal number such as 29. The great insight of the ancient Arabs in developing a number system by marking off positions as powers of ten comes to light here. What is really meant by the decimal number 29 is a direct consequence of this concept of using positions to represent powers of ten. Figure 1.1 illustrates this

$$(29)_{10} = \begin{array}{l} 9 \times 10^0 \rightarrow 9 \\ +2 \times 10^1 \rightarrow 20 \\ \hline (29)_{10} \end{array}$$

Fig. 1.1   The decimal number system

concept. The decimal number 29 means nine times ten to the zeroth power plus two times ten to the first power. The parentheses with the subscript of ten indicate that the number within the parentheses is relative to ten as a base—i.e., a decimal number. Extension of this numbering concept to numbers in the hundreds, thousands, and higher is obvious for members of those offices whose fees run into these ranges.

By direct analogy, one can establish a binary number system based on the concept that positions within a number represent powers of two, rather than ten. Just as a decimal number system has ten digits ranging from zero to nine, so it is natural to expect that a binary number system should have only two digits. Because these two digits have been taken as zero and one, all numbers in a binary number system are composed of these two binary digits, which at first glance makes binary numbers appear rather strange. It should be stressed, however, that it is the *meaning* of a number, rather than its appearance, that is its essential characteristic. The meaning of a binary number like 11101 can be determined by analogy with the decimal number system, each position in the number being treated as a power of two rather than as a power of ten. Figure 1.2 thus indicates that the binary

$$(11101)_2 = \begin{array}{l} 1 \times 2^0 \rightarrow 1 \\ +0 \times 2^1 \rightarrow 0 \\ +1 \times 2^2 \rightarrow 4 \\ +1 \times 2^3 \rightarrow 8 \\ +1 \times 2^4 \rightarrow \underline{16} \\ \hspace{1.6cm} (29)_{10} \end{array}$$

Fig. 1.2   The binary number system

number 11101 means one times two to the zeroth power, plus zero times two to the first power, plus one times two to the second power, plus one times two to the third power, plus one times two to the fourth power. When the binary number 11101 is thus comprehended, it is seen to carry the same *meaning* as the decimal number 29, even though the appearance of the numbers is quite different.

The details and intricacies of number systems such as those presented above are not really important to the discussion here or in the chapters that follow. What is important is the *concept* that one can build numbers in a binary number system out of elements that have only two states—zero or one—and that it is possible to translate these binary numbers into decimal meaning for human consumption. This concept is essential if one is to understand the link between the binary nature of computers and the decimal nature of man's numerical understanding.

1.3   The Basic Components of a Computer

Computers, like toothpaste, automobiles, and design projects, come in three sizes—small, medium, and large. As illustrated in Fig. 1.3, the division between the sizes can be somewhat arbitrarily drawn on the basis of the leasing price of the equipment. Computers leasing for less than about $1,000 per month can be classified as small machines. Machines in this category are normally able to do arithmetic computation reasonably fast and may have some limited logical capabilities. Computers in the $1,000 to $10,000 category can be called intermediate-sized. They generally calculate faster than the smaller machines, have extended logical abilities, and have some form of bulk storage and line-printing facilities available. Machines leasing for over $10,000 per month belong to the large economy class and not only have faster calculation and larger storage facilities but also add extremely high-speed input-output units, graphical displays, capabilities for handling several jobs at once, and hardware features for direct communication from one computer to another. Although rental price is a convenient scale for determining the size and likely general characteristics of a computer, it should by no means be construed as a definition of which computer a firm should use in its practice. As a matter of fact, it is quite likely that a small office would use a large computer, on either a service bureau or time-sharing basis, rather than lease a small computer.

Regardless of the size of the computer, all machines have in common the five basic units shown in Fig. 1.4. The input and output units are the devices on which the normal user's attention is focused, since it is these

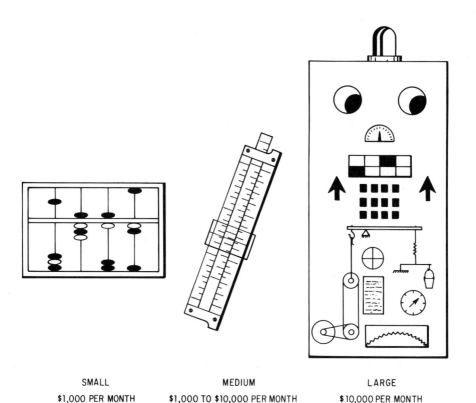

SMALL   MEDIUM   LARGE

$1,000 PER MONTH $1,000 TO $10,000 PER MONTH $10,000 PER MONTH

Fig. 1.3 Computer sizes and costs

Fig. 1.4   The five basic elements of a computer

devices that enable communication between the user and the computer. The memory unit is also sometimes of concern to the user, since it holds the information in which the user is interested. Accordingly, these three units will be discussed in some detail, with examples of typical kinds of units given to illustrate the available speeds and capacities. The arithmetic unit, as expected, is the unit which does the adding, subtracting, multiplying and dividing—usually at the rate of several hundred thousand operations per second in the larger machines. The control unit is responsible for monitoring the flow of information from input and output units to and from the memory and arithmetic units.

To develop some feeling for the types and relative speeds of the various pieces of physical equipment now available, attention will now be turned to three of the conceptual units of computers—input, output, and memory units. Figure 1.5 shows the commonest types of input-output units currently in use, along with their associated speeds for reading information into or out of computer memory. By manually setting certain switches and pushing buttons at the console (the panel with the blinking lights), a computer operator can input one or two digits or alphabetic characters per minute.

	Per minute	Per second
Console	1–2 characters	1/30 characters
Typewriter	60 five-letter words	5
Paper tape	– – –	150
Paper cards	100–1,000 cards	1,300
On-line printer	100–1,000 lines	2,500
Magnetic tape	– – –	100,000
Cathode-ray tube and light pen		

Fig. 1.5   Common types of input-output units

If the computer console is equipped with a typewriter, the operator can input information at normal typing speed, say at about five characters per second. Paper tape is another common input unit, especially on smaller machines, and typically is read at a rate of several hundred characters per second.

By far the commonest input unit is the familiar card reader, which reads from about 100 to 1,000 cards per minute. Since each card can have as many as 80 characters punched on it, it is possible to read information at a rate of about 80,000 characters per minute—or 1,300 per second.

Even this seemingly rapid reading speed is not nearly sufficient for large-scale computers, however. The large machines, in contrast to most humans, think (compute) much faster than they can converse (read and write). Since these large machines typically rent for as much as $500 to $1,000 per hour, it is important to keep them busy thinking as much of the time as possible, and to limit time necessary for conversation (input and output) to a bare minimum. This is a primary reason why magnetic-tape units with their extremely high reading and writing rates of 50,000 to 100,000 characters per second are almost invariably found in large installations for input and output. As a matter of fact, it is normal practice that a medium-sized computer is usually employed as a satellite to a large computer exclusively for the purpose of preparing input magnetic tapes from punched cards and translating output magnetic tapes to the printed page for human consumption. As can be seen in Fig. 1.5, typical output speeds for line printers are something less than 2,000 characters per second, compared with magnetic-tape speeds of 50,000 to 100,000 characters per second.

Figure 1.5 also lists the light pen and cathode-ray tube (the so-called "scope") as input or output units. Practical development of these facilities is just now beginning, and more will be said regarding their use and potential in subsequent chapters.

Before leaving the discussion of input-output units, it is extremely important from a conceptual point of view to make the vital link between the binary nature of computers as discussed earlier and the way in which input-output units operate to translate information from the external world to the internal computer memory. Each type of input-output unit, such as a paper-tape reader, card reader, or magnetic-tape unit, has definite physical characteristics associated with it. These physical characteristics, which are really of a binary nature, are used internally to "store" the information in memory. For card readers, the physical translation mechanism is a series of small wire brushes which pass over the card, punching through the card to make electrical contact with a metal plate whenever a hole is encountered. For paper-tape readers, the mechanism is a photoelectric cell that receives a pulse of light whenever a hole passes the read head. For magnetic-tape readers, the mechanism is a magnetic pickup that senses magnetic spots that occur on the oxide-coated plastic tape as it passes a read head. As might be expected, the electronic pulses which are picked up from the input unit are transmitted to the memory units of the computer, where they are used to "store" the incoming information, generally in the form of magnetization of one form or another.

To illustrate how this hole–no hole, spot–no spot concept can be used to build an intelligibility link between man and machine, Fig. 1.6 shows the standard punch-code scheme for paper cards. Notice that the card is made up of eighty columns, with twelve rows each. Whenever a punch is made in row 1 only, that column is interpreted as a numeric 1. If a punch is made in row 1 and row 12, the column is interpreted as an A. Similar codes exist for all the numbers and letters. As the card passes beneath the small metal

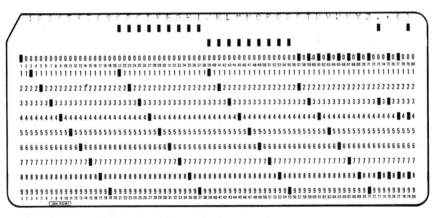

Fig. 1.6   Coding scheme for punched paper cards

brushes in the card reader, the coding is "read" and stored away internally. Thus the external-internal intelligibility link is established. The reader may now amuse himself by interpreting what the next punched card he receives in the mail is really saying about him.

Figure 1.7 shows typical types of memory units currently in use along with their associated capacities and speeds of access. All four types shown

Unit	Storage capacity (8-bit "bytes")	Access time, seconds
Core	10,000–1,000,000	2×10^{-6}
Drum	5,000,000	1×10^{-2}
Disk	10,000,000	1×10^{-2}
Magnetic tape	100,000,000	Up to 1 minute

Fig. 1.7   Common types of memory units

use magnetic principles in the storage of information; i.e., a magnetic spot is either present or not present on the drum, disk, or magnetic tape. By combining a half dozen or so spots (or "bits," for binary digits), one can establish internal codes for decimal numbers and alphabetic characters. When these digits and characters are strung together in appropriate ways, words can be formed, and the external link of communication to man is thereby reestablished.

Of the four types of computer units shown, core storage is normally considered primary, or working, storage. The drums, disks, and tapes are normally considered secondary, or bulk, storage. The reasons for these designations are to be found in the capacities and access times of the units. Core storage, which is the most expensive to build, is by far the fastest in terms of being able to retrieve a piece of information. Typically, access time is of the order of two or three millionths of a second, compared with an access time ten thousand times slower for disks and drums. Because of the size and costs of core storage, however, it is not well suited for the storage of bulk information such as voluminous lists of material properties, financial data, or specification texts. Accordingly, most medium- and large-sized computers employ core storage for the information which is currently being processed, and supplement this core storage with some type of secondary bulk storage. As one would expect, of course, transfer of information between the various types of storage units is very easily and efficiently done.

1.4   Levels of Man-Machine Communication

It is evident from the preceding discussion that there is a great gap between the precise binary yes-no, hole–no hole requirements for computer processing and the normal communicative language of mankind. Without question, this gap has been a primary reason for the aura of mystery that has sometimes surrounded computers in the past. Once one understands the basic binary nature of computers as discussed in the previous section, the mystery is reduced to a problem of levels of communication and translation between those levels.

Figure 1.8 shows four main levels for communication between man and

Fig. 1.8   Levels of man-machine communication

machine that have developed in the brief history of the computer age. The first level, strictly binary, is the most difficult for man to use. In the early 1950s, however, this was the only level available, and all programming was done with the binary digits of zero and one. There is rumor of a marked increase in the admission rates at mental health institutions during the early fifties.

Inasmuch as it quickly became evident that the binary programs so laboriously produced by remarkably patient men were capable of performing rather intricate accounting and clerical tasks, the idea was not long in forthcoming that the machine itself could be used as a translator from a language that was more convenient for man to the binary language demanded by the machine. Such an idea produced the second level of communication shown in Fig. 1.8, the assembly level (also sometimes called the symbolic level). To add two numbers A and B together, and to store the result in X, it is obviously easier to write the symbolic instructions shown in the illustration than it is to write the equivalent string of zeros and ones required at the machine-language level. Although only a relatively small group of those who use computers today are required to use symbolic-level programming, it remains the basic level of communication upon which higher levels ultimately depend.

Perhaps the most familiar level of man-machine communication is the compiler level, of which FORTRAN is the best-known example. The problem of adding A and B together to form X is written at this level in an arithmetic formula, as shown in the illustrations, and the machine does the necessary translation to binary machine language. For most types of problems that depend heavily on mathematical processing, compiler-level languages provide great flexibility and ease of use. Accordingly, this level of communication has found wide acceptance.

By now it is clear that the higher the level of man-machine communication that man can use, the easier is the task of communicating to the computer. This is particularly true at the fourth level of communication shown in Fig. 1.8. At this level, man is able to use English-language phrases, such as the one illustrated, to issue commands to the computer. This kind of communication ability tends to develop around a particular problem type, or academic discipline, and is therefore called a problem-oriented language.

The earliest such language, COGO, was in the problem area of coordinate geometry and was developed by Prof. C. L. Miller and his associates at M.I.T. in the early 1960s. A Structural Engineering Systems Solver (STRESS), developed by Fenves, Logcher, Mauch, and others at M.I.T., has found wide acceptance within the structural-engineering community. Numerous other problem-oriented languages (frequently abbreviated POLs) are under development and will undoubtedly have a profound effect on the architectural and engineering professions. Two such languages, PROJECT for project control through networking techniques such as CPM and PERT, and BUILD for architectural purposes, are discussed at some length in Chapters 7 and 9.

Although the STRESS language and its successor STRUDL will be discussed more fully in Chapter 3, a few typical commands from the language at this point may help the reader to gain some feeling for the type of language intended and its obvious ease of use. For example, the commands given in Fig. 1.9, when coupled with others of like nature, are sufficient to instruct the computer to perform a wind analysis for wind blowing on the long face of a structure called the Hancock Center.

```
STRUCTURE  HANCOCK  CENTER
JOINT COORDINATES
1  X  0.  Y  0.  Z  0.
2  ...
   ...
MEMBER INCIDENCES
1  1  2
   ...
MEMBER PROPERTIES
   ...
LOADING 1  WIND ON LONG FACE
JOINT LOADS
   ...
SOLVE
```

Fig. 1.9   **Examples of commands from the STRESS language**

Before leaving the discussion of the various levels of man-machine communication, it may be instructive to review schematically the translation process as it occurs in the machine.

The concept of translation is itself, of course, quite simple. Suppose, for example, that one wishes to add the two members A and B and to store the result in location X. Figure 1.10 shows the appropriate FORTRAN (compiler-level) language statement to accomplish this task. The equivalent

Compiler level (source)		Assembly level		Binary level (object)
		CLA A		11000 00001
X = A + B	→	AD B	→	10000 00010
		STO X		11010 00011

Fig. 1.10   **The concept of language translation**

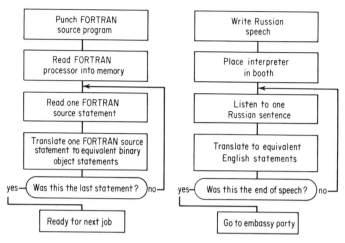

Fig. 1.11   Translation of the FORTRAN and Russian languages

assembly-level statements are also shown, as are the end-product binary-level machine-language statements. Given sufficient syntactical rules, translation from a higher-level language such as FORTRAN to a lower-level language is thus strictly mechanical.

The translation from a compiler (source) language to machine (object) language is similar to the translation of a speech at the United Nations from Russian (source language) to English (object language). Figure 1.11 shows the steps in the mechanism of translation from a FORTRAN source program to the binary object program. Also included in the figure are the counterparts of this process in translation from Russian to English.

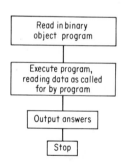

Fig. 1.12   The execution of a machine-language program

Once the original FORTRAN program has been translated, the object program can be used repeatedly to solve the problem at hand. In other words, the translation process occurs just once, even though the program may be used many times to solve problems with different data. Figure 1.12 indicates schematically the execution of a program that has at some time in the past been translated to machine language.

1.5   An Example FORTRAN Problem

Although it is by no means the purpose either of this chapter or of the remaining portions of the book to serve as a computer text, the following

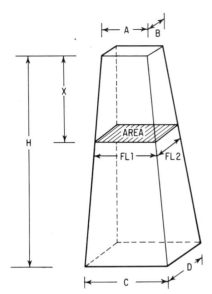

Fig. 1.13 Schematic perspective of the 100-story Hancock Center

elementary example is given as an indication of the kind of FORTRAN statements that one would write to solve typical architectural and engineering problems.

Figure 1.13 shows a geometrical representation of a building such as the 100-story Hancock Center in Chicago. The building is tapered on all four sides and has dimensions A, B, C, D, and H as shown. The problem is to read one card per story, compute the floor area at that level X, and see if that floor area exceeds 40,000 square feet. If it does, print out the message "FLOOR AREA EXCEEDS 40000 SQ. FT." The total building area should also be printed out. Figure 1.14 shows the FORTRAN source program which solves the problem. The uppercase statements on the left are the actual FORTRAN statements which are punched into cards. The lowercase statements on the right are comments to the reader to explain the function of the FORTRAN statements on the left.

```
C    COMPUTATION OF FLOOR AREAS FOR HANCOCK CENTER
C
     PRINT 8 ---------------------- Prints title
     SUMA = 0. ------------------- Sets a location = 0
     DO 5 1 = I,  100 ------------- Begins loop for 100 stories
     READ 7,  A, B, C, D, H, X ------- Reads data
     FL1 = A + X/H * (C–A)  ⎤
     FL2 = B + X/H * (D–B)  ⎥
     AREA = FL1 * FL2        ⎬ -------- Computes floor area
     SUMA = SUMA + AREA  ⎦
     PRINT 15,  AREA ---------------- Prints floor area
     IF (AREA–40000.) 5, 5, 4 --------- Tests to see if AREA > 40,000 sq ft
```

```
 5   CONTINUE
     GO TO 3
 4   PRINT 16 _____ Prints message "floor area exceeds
 3   PRINT 17, SUMA                  40,000 sq ft"
     PAUSE _____ Stops
 7   FORMAT (6F10.2)                              ⎤ Information
 8   FORMAT (31 H HANCOCK CENTER AREA            ⎪ on how
       COMPUTATION)                              ⎬ input-output
15   FORMAT (5HAREA = , F12.0, 6H SQ FT)         ⎪ data are to
16   FORMAT (//32 H FLOOR AREA EXCEEDS 40,000 SQ FT//) ⎦ appear
17   FORMAT (//19 H SUM OF FLOOR AREAS = F 12.0,
       6H SQ FT)
     END
```

Fig. 1.14   Example FORTRAN program for floor-area computations

1.6   Conclusion

The foregoing pages have sketched very briefly some of the basic computer fundamentals which eventually are at the root of every application problem. Throughout the remainder of the text, attention will be turned toward practical application of these fundamentals to the solution of problems in office management, engineering, specifications, estimating, accounting, networking, and architecture.

CHAPTER TWO *Organization*
and Function of a Computer
in a Design Office

By Charles F. Beck

*Once an office has, by one means or another, acquainted itself with
basic computer fundamentals, it has taken the initial step toward
development of a computer capability. A broader discussion of what
this concept means, and its implications for the organizational form of
the design office, is the subject matter of Chapter 2. This chapter also
offers a wide range of suggestions on the daily problems of computer
operations, ranging from initiation of computer programs to
economics of computer utilization.*

Mr. Beck is an Associate of Sargent & Lundy,
Engineers, in Chicago, and head of their
Analytical and Computer Division. He has been
with the firm since 1948 as a designer of
power-plant structures, and has been active in
computer applications since 1957. Mr. Beck
holds a B.S. degree in Civil Engineering from
the Illinois Institute of Technology. He is a
member of ASCE, ACM, and several other
professional groups. He is a registered Structural
Engineer in Illinois. Mr. Beck has been head of
the firm's Computer Division since its formation
in 1963 and is responsible for development
and application of computer techniques for
solving engineering design problems.

2.1 Introduction

The relationship of the professional engineer or architect to the computer is such that they are inseparable. With the computer the engineer or architect has every opportunity to extend his capabilities to do imaginative and creative work. The degree of interaction between man and the computer in the design process is what we define as computer capability.

Computer capability means having the ability, facilities, programs, and personnel to implement computer techniques in the solution of design problems. People must be instructed and trained in the computer sciences, and computer facilities must be convenient for their use. Designers and programmers must collaborate to produce computer programs. Management and designers must be indoctrinated in the philosophy of the computer program so that it will be properly implemented in the design. Computer capability is an integrated system in which all these factors contribute and interact. This capability does not come with the purchase of a computer, nor is it part of any computer program library—it must be developed.

The mechanics and methods for developing a computer capability are presented in this chapter. The material and philosophies outlined have evolved over a period of time since 1954; they reflect the actual experience and practices in implementing these concepts at Sargent & Lundy.

The computer installation at Sargent & Lundy would be considered medium-sized. However, the fundamental principles and concepts described in this chapter are as applicable to a two-man design office as they are to a large-scale engineering service bureau operation.

2.2 Development of a Computer Capability

Paramount to the development of a computer capability the designer must thoroughly understand the design process and the computer's role in it.

The practice of engineering or architecture is a mixture of applied science and art. As a rule, there is no direct procedure leading to a solution of a specific design problem. Consequently, the design process is normally one of iteration whereby the designer defines his problem and develops a conceptual design based upon his knowledge and experience. He must then construct and analyze a mathematical model of the problem by imposing environmental design conditions. The response of the model is compared with a predetermined standard of acceptance which may be

based upon the material used, economics, aesthetics, or fabrication requirements, construction details, etc.

If the design does not conform to the acceptance criteria, the designer
may change one or several design parameters and repeat the process.
Obtaining the best solution or optimum design is frequently a function of
the number of iterations of the design process, the number of refinements
made, and the time available. With the aid of a computer in this highly
iterative design process, the designer can achieve a better solution—more
economically and more quickly.

The fundamental decisions are still the responsibility of the designer.
He must define and specify his problem, produce a conceptual design,
construct a mathematical model, determine the environmental conditions,
prepare computer input, validate the results, establish the acceptance
criteria, and supervise the entire process.

The design process is an integrated system in which management, engineering design staff, programmer, computer, and the computer program
library all contribute and interact as depicted in Fig. 2.1. The degree of
interaction is defined as computer capability.

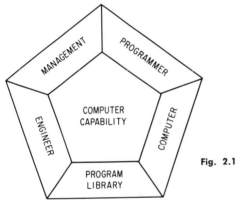

Fig. 2.1   Integrated system

One does not develop a computer capability immediately or overnight,
but rather over a period of time—for it involves implementing a new
design tool and consequently overcoming the inertia toward change in
design-office practices.

Management's role in developing a computer capability cannot be overemphasized. A year-long study[1] of the current and future uses of computers in 33 successful manufacturing firms in the United States found that
the firms with the most successful computer operations were those in
which management was vitally interested and actively participated in the
operation. The men who managed these operations were experienced in
the company's design philosophy and procedures as well as having a

marked degree of competence in computer technology. The success of a computer operation is proportional to the degree that management is committed and all echelons of management participate in the program.

Some of management's greatest responsibilities are to specify the objectives correctly, make adequate plans, and formulate policies for the integration of computer techniques. To do this management must take the systems approach in evaluating the computer's role. Management must have a clear view of what is needed and what is potentially feasible. They must have a closely reasoned determination of the best course for achieving the desired results. They must also have a dependable measure of the means already available and of those which must be developed in order to make feasible the goals that are to be achieved. The systems approach to overall management leads to the integrated systems concept. No longer are engineering divisions and departments acting separately. Instead, they must be fused into an overall system, which again points out the fact that the computer operation has to have the level of authority where main-stream decisions are made in the firm. The computer operation is definitely a *line function* in the organizational structure. Interrelationship of computer activities with other functions will influence thinking about the need to position computer responsibilities as part of a broadened top-management functional area.

2.3   Implementation of Computer Technology

Before one can begin to implement computer technology in a design office, its mechanism or operational structure must be thoroughly understood.

Previous to the advent of the computer, the design-office structure consisted of three major functions: project managers, design and drafting, and management, as shown in Fig. 2.2.

With the development of a computer capability within an office, it is reasonable to anticipate a certain amount of reorganization of the office

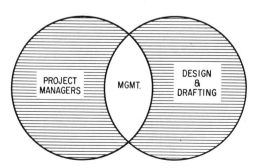

Fig. 2.2   Design-office structure

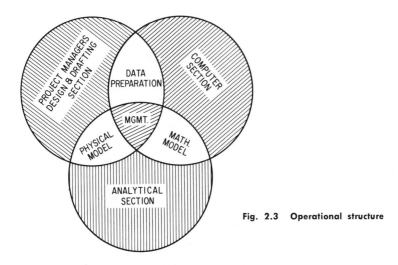

Fig. 2.3   Operational structure

structure. The operational structure must take advantage of the knowledge and talents of specialists and technicians, as shown in Fig. 2.3.

The project managers, design engineers, and draftsmen are basically project-oriented and have full responsibility for the job. They implement the design and analysis performed by the analytical and computer groups. The analytical section is fundamentally problem-oriented, and their approach to the design will emphasize the formulation of the mathematical model to simulate the physical problem. The computer section is concerned with the development and writing of the program to correspond to the mathematical model of the design problem.

It would be idealistic to assume that each of these three functions exists as a separate entity. This is especially true in small offices where all three functions may be performed by only one or two people. Conceptually, however, there are areas of overlapping, as shown in the figure. Note that all three functions overlap in the central area of management. This seems particularly appropriate since final responsibility for the organization's success or failure must rest with management. Management must coordinate and supervise the entire operation, provide realistic goals to attain, evaluate performances, establish budgetary controls, and develop and administer office standard procedures and practices.

2.4   Organization and Staffing of a Computer Section

The organization of a computer section for a design office is in a sense difficult to define. This is due to the nature of design, and because a major portion of the engineering and architectural profession is relatively new to the field of computer sciences.

The practice of engineering or architecture is a combination of applied science and art and therefore is not easily expressed to a computer. Early engineering applications were mainly analysis-type programs simply because they were easiest to write. The actual physical structure could be accurately defined by a mathematical model. However, writing a program to perform engineering or architectural design is much more difficult because it involves a design philosophy. Philosophy cannot be translated to a computer in general terms; it must be defined accurately, specifically, and in a step-by-step logical sequence. The individual firm's interpretation of philosophy is often the deciding factor in the application of a building code or design specification to a design problem.

The tasks necessary to define an application for computer solution and to process the data can be performed by one person or may be divided among several people. One person must be familiar with the problem in order to define it properly. Another might define the broad outline for computer-assisted solution, another do the programming, and still another operate the computer to process the data. The functional organization of such a computer group is shown in Fig. 2.4.

In a small design office or in one just beginning to initiate computer techniques, almost all the functions depicted in Fig. 2.4 will be performed by one or two persons. As computer capability is developed and the program library grows, the staff and the use of the computer facilities will be quite likely to expand.

The size of a computer staff also varies with the mode of operation. For example, when the computer is used in "closed-shop" arrangement, where

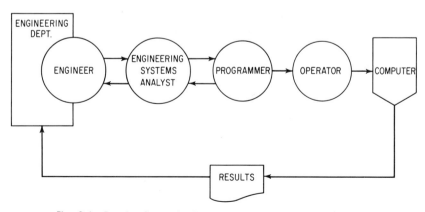

Fig. 2.4   Functional organization

a full-time staff does all the systems analysis and programming and operates the equipment, a larger staff is required. For an "open-shop" operation, in which the analysis, programming, and operation are done by various members within the section originating the application, the size of the staff may be considerably smaller.

In an engineering design office the operating philosophy is usually somewhere between the "closed-shop" and "open-shop" arrangement.

In considering an organizational structure for a computer section the only precedent available is the commercial installation, which is shown in Fig. 2.5.

Basically, the computer section depicted is comprised of three major functions: analysis, programming, and operations.

The analysis section defines and interprets the problem for computer-aided solution. The systems analyst prepares a system flow chart showing the interrelation of man and computer in the problem solution.

The programming section interprets the system flow chart into a detail flow chart and codes the problem.

The operations section schedules the work, operates the peripheral equipment to process the data, and maintains the program library.

However, such an organizational structure is not practical in an engineering or architectural environment because of the nature and complexity of the design problems. Engineering or architectural installations generally have a large variety and number of applications programmed which require a relatively small amount of data to be processed, whereas a commercial installation will have a few major applications programmed

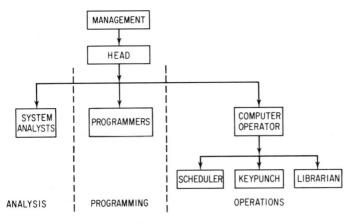

Fig. 2.5   Organizational structure

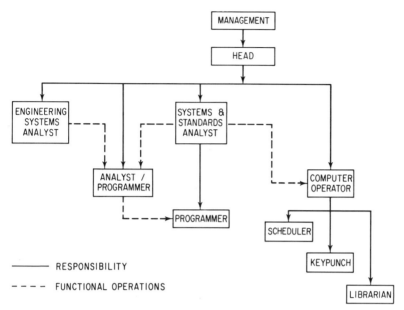

Fig. 2.6   Organizational structure for a design office

but process a large volume of data. Therefore, the organizational structure and the job functions have a different connotation.

The organization depicted in Fig. 2.6 is more representative of a computer section for an engineering or architectural firm.

It is not always possible to define and analyze the problem well enough to communicate the philosophy to another person who will do the programming. Thus the analyst/programmer, by necessity, will be required to do systems-analysis work as well as programming. His educational background and training should reflect the discipline for which he is programming. He will also be indispensable in directing its implementation on a project because of his intimate knowledge of the program.

As the size of the computer staff increases, it will be well to consider the addition of a systems programmer. He would be oriented toward computer sciences more than an applications programmer and would act as a systems and standards analyst. His knowledge of the intricacies of the computing system and program languages would be very helpful to the staff in writing more efficient programs and also assisting in the debugging phases.

In order for the reader to have a feel for the scope, duties, and responsibility of each function shown in Fig. 2.6, a detailed job definition and description for each function is given. The intent is to give some insight into what is involved and what is to be expected in performing these functions. The descriptions themselves are very general and should not in any way be considered conclusive. They are the result of a study the writer made to derive job descriptions for his own use. The only published job descriptions[2, 3, 4] available to date are concerned with commercial and scientific installations. Again, it is emphasized that these job descriptions are as applicable to a small office with one or two persons as they are to a larger installation. In a small office, many of these functions will be performed by the same person.

The *head of the computer section* should, if possible, be appointed from within the firm. This is desirable for many reasons. First, he knows almost everyone in the firm, and this will tend to simplify communications. He will also be familiar with the company design philosophy which will be helpful in implementing computer techniques. Management will rely on his judgment regarding the purchasing of a computer for developing of programming and, in general, establishing a computer capability.

His duties and responsibilities will include liaison between management and the computer group; staffing and supervising the analysts and programmers; outlining the scope for specifications of the programs to be written; establishing systems and standards procedures to be used by the group; being responsible for editing the documentation or programs and for the integrity of programs produced; planning, scheduling, and monitoring the work; and compiling statistics and making reports concerning the progress of the programming effort. He should also evaluate job performances.

The *engineering systems analyst* plans and develops computer programs from the problem specification and criteria outlined by the head of the computer division and the engineer submitting the application. He determines the numerical solution most suitable for the particular application; develops the block diagrams showing interrelationship of the engineer, the computer, and other related functions; designs input and output formats; supervises the programming and coding for the computer; and sets up a test problem for debugging and testing the program. He is responsible for documenting the work and supervising programmers and computer technicians. He is thoroughly familiar with the policy requirements and operating needs of the firm.

The *analyst/programmer* works under the direction of the engineering systems analyst; he assists in defining the problem, preparing the systems flow charts, designing input and output formats, and conjuring problems to test and debug the program. He also prepares detail flow charts and codes the problem, assists the systems analyst in debugging and testing programs, and contributes and supervises the documentation. On larger programs he may be able to segment the program and supervise programming effort.

The *systems and standards analyst* is responsible for initiating and maintaining programming systems. He should set up, develop, and maintain a systems and standards manual for the section. He sees that the policies and procedures specified in the manual are followed. This person must have a thorough working knowledge of the various programming languages such as FORTRAN, assembly language, and machine language for several different types of computers. He assists the engineering systems analyst in the development of a computer application from a standpoint of maximum utilization of the hardware and programming languages. The systems and standards analyst teaches programming courses to engineers and other members of the firm, besides training and supervising the various members of the programming staff. He may be involved in any aspect of programming requiring intimate knowledge of computer hardware and programming languages.

The *programmer* prepares the detail flow charts and codes the problem in the language suited for the particular application and computer from the systems flow charts prepared by the analyst.

The *operator* operates the computer and all input-output equipment to process the work. He follows the operating procedures outlined in the program documentation and makes notes of any malfunction of the computer or the program during the execution of a program; his notes on the incident will be interrogated by the programmer. Knowledge of programming is helpful in making an interrogation of malfunction. The operator should be familiar with various operating routines for obtaining diagnostics, traces, and dumps to aid in the debugging phases. Being familiar with the various components of the hardware so he can repair any minor breakdowns is important. He should know how to operate peripheral equipment such as keypunch, reproducer, and sorter and do minor card punching and setup work prior to processing.

The *scheduler's* main responsibility is to schedule the work to ensure that the computer system is effectively and efficiently used. He attempts to keep all unused time to a minimum by maintaining a liaison with the section head and reassigning unused time. The scheduler coordinates preventive maintenance with operating requirements, processes the input data forms for keypunch, establishes liaison with service bureaus for work done on outside computers, schedules time on these computers, and arranges for the work to be sent out. He keeps records on all transactions taking place in the computer section and the computer time used outside, so that computer costs can be reconciled and allocated. He keeps the "turnaround" time to an absolute minimum; in other words, he minimizes time to process the problem from receipt of the data forms until the results are returned to the design engineer. The scheduler also keeps a log on all supplies, such as cards, paper forms, and ribbons, and reorders when it is necessary.

The *librarian* is responsible for maintaining and updating the company application library. The librarian catalogs the programs and documentation, and issues periodically the program catalog containing application abstracts. He keeps the program source decks filed and current and keeps a record of information and programs stored on disk files. The librarian establishes liaison and keeps contact with the program libraries of the manufacturers, universities and colleges, user groups, etc.; files and updates the manufacturer's computer reference library; orders manuals and other literature from the computer manufacturer; keeps and maintains the office systems and standards manual; files and keeps current newsletters from the various user-group organizations; and circulates and keeps tabs on periodicals and reports routed to the staff members.

The *keypunch operator* operates the alphanumeric keypunch and verifier. She keypunches and verifies from standard input data forms or directly from source documents. The keypunch operators are expected to know most of the procedures for routine work and be imaginative enough to assist in the planning of input formats for new applications.

A computer section such as that shown in Fig. 2.6 should be staffed with people who have degrees in engineering or architecture or the equivalent, and preferably have experience in actual design practice. It is much simpler to teach an engineer or architect how to program than it is to hire professional computer programmers or mathematicians and teach them engineering or architecture. Today most graduates of engineering and architectural schools have had some experience with the FORTRAN language and some familiarity with numerical-analysis techniques in their undergraduate work. This type of staff will provide a vital and necessary communication linkage between the design engineer and the computer.

Recruiting personnel for a computer staff will be a difficult task because of the great demand for computer programmers,[5] particularly those having engineering backgrounds. As of March, 1967, there are approximately 35,000 computers installed and in use for commercial, scientific, engineering, and process-control applications. It is expected that the number of computers installed will increase to 60,000 in 1970 and to 80,000 by 1975. With this projected increase in computer usage the demand for computer-trained people[6] to staff these installations will increase exponentially.

The most likely sources to recruit these people are at universities and colleges or from within the firm.

One aid in the selection of individuals for training as computer programmers is the IBM Aptitude Test for Programmer Personnel (ATPP).[7] The ATPP test is basically a test of reasoning ability and consists of three sub-tests: a letter-series test, a figure-series test, and an arithmetical-reasoning test. The test is constructed so that the ability to solve the problem is a more important factor than speed. One hour is required to administer the test.

Once the individual has been hired, all the normal personnel practices should be followed. It is especially important that his work be reviewed and evaluated periodically. He should be informed as to his progress and status on the staff. Constructive criticism should be given when necessary. Recognition of his work and achievements should be made. He should also be encouraged to publish his work.

Salaries[2, 3, 4, 8] are difficult to determine and establish for a number of reasons. The area in which the firm is located is one important factor. For example, there is a greater demand for computer-trained people on the East Coast and the West Coast than in the Middle West, which influences the wage scale. The proximity of the firm to universities and colleges for continuing education is another factor. Other considerations are fringe benefits, educational opportunities, the working environment, and perhaps most important the challenge of the work to be performed and the computer facilities available.

Educational background and years of professional as well as programming experience will have an important influence on salary ranges. A compilation of the results in recent (1967) surveys[2, 3, 4, 8] indicates the salary ranges shown in Table 2.1.

TABLE 2.1 Salary Ranges

Job function	Installation	Salary
1. Systems analyst_____	Commercial	$7,000 to $12,500 per year
	Engineering	$400 to $700 per year more than his equivalent professional rank or grade
2. Analyst/programmer____	Commercial	No Comparable position
	Engineering	$400 to $700 per year more than his equivalent professional rank or grade
3. Programmer_____	Commercial	$6,500 to $11,000 per year
	Engineering	$7,300 to $12,000 per year
4. Computer operator_____		$5,500 to $9,000 per year
5. Scheduler_____		$6,500 to $7,500 per year
6. Keypunch operator_____		$3,600 to $6,000 per year

2.5   Initiation of a Computer Program

The firm should have a policy for reviewing and approving program application requests proposed by members of the staff in order to comprehend fully the implications of implementing a new computer program. Such a policy will also ensure the most productive use of the computer facilities and staff. In addition, management will be directly involved and assume a share of responsibility for the allocation of the firm's resources in terms of manpower and materials.

The mechanics of initiating a computer program application are illustrated by the flow chart shown in Fig. 2.7.

The operations and procedures indicated in Fig. 2.7 may be performed automatically by responsible people in a small office or may be performed by many people in a larger installation in a more formal manner. The principles are basic and apply in either case.

The major points in the process are the application request, the feasibility study, and the disposition of the request.

The program application request may originate with any engineer or individual in the firm. This person presents and discusses with the department manager his ideas for a computer program which he feels will be valuable to the firm. If the manager concurs with the suggestion and feels that it has merit, he will approve the request, initiating a feasibility study.

The feasibility study should be made by a person thoroughly familiar with the problem and by computer personnel. The study consists of defining the problem, the engineering design philosophy to be used in its solution, the method for numerical solution, a library search for existing computer programs, an economic evaluation, consideration of the tangible and intangible benefits, and a recommendation to management.

The disposition of the request can be made by a management review committee or by the official responsible for the computer section. In either case there must be an awareness of the other programs being developed or written and the urgency of this new application. Management must decide where the resources and effort should be expended. To aid in making a decision all program applications approved or being developed are listed on a priority-assignment form as shown in Fig. 2.8. A periodic review of this list should be made and priorities assigned or reassigned depending upon the work schedule.

To aid management and others in making the evaluation of a program application submitted by an engineer an instrument such as the program application request form shown in Fig. 2.9 may be used.

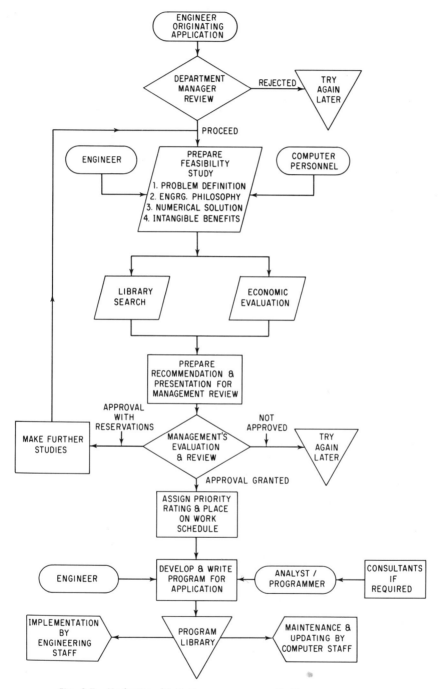

Fig. 2.7   Mechanics of initiating a program application

Req. No.	Computer application	Req. by	Date	Auth. by and date	Program title	Acq. No.
1	Piping flexibility	Mech. Analy.	3/16		Piping-flexibility analysis	36
2	Computer services usage record-keeping program	Computer Div.	9/1		Computer services report generator	48
3	Accounting department functions	Account. Dept.	April		Bimonthly payroll	55
4	Structural design program	Struct. Dept.	May		Beam edit	50
					Beam selection	51
					Composite beam	52
					Deflection	53
5	Tower-spotting program	Struct. Dept.	10/6		Edison's transmission tower spotting	
6	Specifications	Struct.	8/16			
7	Nuclear heat balance	Nuclear and Mech. Analy.	9/27		Nuclear heat balance	
8	Insulator-offset clipping calculation	Elec. Analy. Division	10/12		Insulator-offset clipping calculation	56
9	Ruling-span calculation	Elec. Analy. Division	11/2		Ruling-span calculation	57
10	Wiring-stringing chart calculations	Elec. Analy. Division	11/16		Wire string chart calculations	58
11	Lake-evaporation study	Struct.	March			
12	Edison load flow	Elec. Analy.	11/5/65		Edison load flow	
13	Vibration analysis for piping system	Mech. Analy.	11/17/65			
14	Economic study CCI and VPP	Elec. Analy.	11/16/65			
15	Short-circuit studies	Elec. Analy.	11/18/65			

Fig. 2.8   Priority-assignment form

This document will serve as the vehicle for recording the proceedings and transactions of the procedures outlined in Fig. 2.7.

It should be understood that this request form is only an aid in making the evaluation and should not be considered as the sole criterion in decision making. Other considerations weigh heavily in these evaluations. Intangible benefits such as being able to extend the creative abilities of

Program No.	Computer systems	Problem analyst	Systems analyst/ programmer	Date started	Date released	Remarks
9.5.006	1130	Tony Porvit	L. Kvitek	9/20		Conversion of 1620 program to 1130 computer previous time charged to 3218-1
10.9.001	1130	C. F. Beck	R. Ruth S. F. Fok	9/1		
10.5.001	1130	R. W. Rowe H. G. Souden S. Dombrowski	C. F. Beck			
9.7.020	1130	C. F. Beck/S. L. Chu	S. L. Chu/J. Harty			
9.7.021	1130	C. F. Beck/S. L. Chu	S. L. Chu/J. Harty			
9.7.022	1130	C. F. Beck/S. L. Chu	S. L. Chu/J. Harty			
9.7.023	1130	C. F. Beck/S. L. Chu	S. L. Chu/J. Harty			
	7094	C. F. Beck				
9.5.007	7094/1130		S. F. Fok			
9.4.014	7094/1130	C. C. Pallardy	R. Ruth	10/12		
9.4.015	7094/1130	C. C. Pallardy	R. Ruth	11/2		
9.4.016	7094/1130	C. C. Pallardy	R. Ruth	11/16		
	7094/1130	R. N. Bergstrom				
	7094	L. B. LeVesconte R. X. French	S. F. Fok			Seminar H. Brown 11/12/65 L. B. LeVesconte letter requesting program 11/65
	7094/1130	C. Hatstat	S. F. Fok			
	7094/1130	C. Hatstat				

the engineering staff and being able to reduce the engineering man-hours to do a design as well as providing management with better information are some of the major considerations.

Approval of the program application request initiates the writing of a new computer program or the validating of a program obtained from some computer library. The engineer who submitted the request is assigned to work with the computer section in developing and writing the program.

I. *Application Request*

  A. Title of Computer Application:

  B. Request by: Date:

  C. Approved by: Date:

II. *Feasibility Study*

  A. Problem definition (use separate sheet if necessary to adequately define and describe application to be programmed)

  B. Design philosophy to be used in solution of problem:

  C. Technique for numerical solution:

  D. Intangible Benefits:

  E. Estimate of time for manual solution of problem

    1. Assemble source data . . . . _____ manhours

    2. Perform calculations . . . . _____ manhours

    3. Checking of assumptions made and the calculations . . . . _____ manhours

    4. Number of times problem will occur in the period under consideration . . . . . . _____ times/period

  F. Library Search

    1. Programs available:

  G. Estimate of time required for programming application

    _____ new program

    _____ validating existing library program

    _____ update existing program

    1. Complete problem definition . . . . . _____ manhours

    2. Systems design

      a. systems flow chart . . . . . _____

      b. input & output format design . _____

      c. test problems . . . . . . _____

      d. documentation . . . . . . _____

                                _____ manhours

    3. Programming

      a. detail flow chart . . . . . _____

      b. coding . . . . _____

      c. documentation . . . . . . _____

                                _____ manhours

    4. Testing and debugging . . . . _____ manhours

    5. Total programming effort . . . . _____ manhours

    6. Time required to enter parameters onto input forms . . . . _____ manhours

  H. Economic Evaluation

    1. Engineering manhour time that is expected to be saved through the use of the program:

      $(E2 + E3 - G6) \times (E4) =$

      $(\ +\ -\ ) \times (\ ) = $ . . . . . . _____ manhours

    2. Number of times program will have to be used in order to break even:

      $(G5) \div (E2 + E3 - G6) =$

      $(\ ) \div (\ +\ -\ ) = $ . . . . . _____

  I. Additional comments or remarks concerning program application for management review committee consideration:

III. *Disposition of Program Application Request:*
    A. Program application approved by: Date:
        1. Assigned Program No.
        2. Priority No.
    B. Tabled for review at later date by: Date:
    C. Program application shows promise but further study is required in
        these areas:
                by: Date:

Fig. 2.9   Program application request form

After the program is written and accepted by the engineering department, it is placed in the program library. From this point on the program will be implemented by the engineering staff. The computer section will be responsible for maintaining and updating the program as required and processing the data.

2.6   Classification and Types of Computer Programs

The phrase "computer program" has become a generic term which includes a wide range and classification of programs. In design applications these programs are so varied in complexity that it becomes difficult to classify them in order to evaluate their economic worth. To date there is no established standard by which to measure the value of a program. The value becomes important when attempting to trade or purchase a program or when hiring an outside source to program a particular application. A rule-of-thumb measure could be the number of FORTRAN coding statements in the program or the number of man-hours used in developing and coding the program.

The types of program are as varied as the types of problems encountered in design and range over an entire spectrum of complexity. At the lower end of the scale are the simple programs such as the evaluation of a mathematical function, solving a set of simultaneous equations, fitting a curve to the results of some test data, or generating a set of tables for quick reference. An engineer exposed to a short course in FORTRAN can usually write this type of program with a minimum of difficulty. The solution is not sophisticated and the engineer does not have to be a "computer expert." The program may consist of a small number of FORTRAN statements and require a minimum number of man-hours to code. The computer time required to process this class of program is negligible. A major distinction is that design philosophy is not a consideration. A large portion of most program libraries consists of this class of program. Usually such programs become subroutines of larger and more complex system-type programs.

At the upper end of the spectrum are the more complex system-type programs such as those required for the analysis and design of structures; determining the heating and ventilating loads for a building; making a study of an electrical distribution system; or determining the optimum proportion of the height, width, and floor area of a structure considering economics and building-systems interfacing. This class of program is more sophisticated and requires management involvement and appraisal. The solution of this type of problem requires a systems approach in which each element of the problem is evaluated relative to the entire problem.

A firm's design philosophy and procedures are major considerations. A great deal of programming effort is involved, which may require many persons with various talents and skills. The systems-type programs are more costly to write in terms of man-hours and computer time. Some programs of this type may contain several thousand coding statements. The STRESS, COGO, and ICES programs are examples of this classification.

2.7   Program Documentation

The importance of proper documentation for computer programs cannot be overemphasized. The failure or success of any computer installation will be largely dependent on its ability to communicate the program application and to disseminate the work to the users. This can be accomplished only by adequately documenting the work, by holding seminars, or by offering courses to educate the engineering staff and the potential user. The program is only as good as the documentation.

Proper documentation is also necessary when exchanging programs with other computer installations or when contributing to users-group libraries. Without a proper write-up one can hardly expect to negotiate with others for programs.

Many city agencies regulating building codes have specific standards for program documentation.[9] If a computer is used in any phase of the design calculation, the documentation must conform to the agency's standards and be submitted with the computer calculations to obtain a construction license or permit. In addition, it is sometimes required that sample problems be submitted, solved by the computer, and verified and supported by manual computation.

Documentation is the only means of perpetuating the use of a program in a firm. This is particularly important in view of the personnel turnover within a computer installation and the shortage of programmers.

In the preparation of documentation the author should keep in mind that to implement the program properly several people may be involved, each with his own interpretation of the document, educational background, and function. These people are management, the user, the operator, and the programmer.

For simple programs, a one-page program abstract may be sufficient. However, for the "systems" type program, an entire set of documentation may be required such as:

1. Program abstract
2. Applications description
3. User's manual
4. Operator's manual
5. Programmer's manual

Documentation for most engineering and architectural programs usually is of an intermediate nature, with a few written pages and listing frequently being sufficient.

To provide a brief summary of the application for the firm's library it is desirable to prepare at least a program abstract. The abstract should be written so that it gives a general idea of what the searcher will find by reading the more complete documentation (if such exists), and so that the potential user can determine whether the program is likely to be applicable to his needs.

The abstract should not exceed one typewritten page in length and should be exact, concise, and nonambiguous. The following format is recommended:

1. Title
2. Program number
3. Author
4. Program scope and computational approach used
5. Brief description of input
6. Brief description of output
7. Machine configuration
8. Estimate of running time

For many of the programs in the firm's library, it will also be necessary to prepare an applications description. This description is a little more elaborate than a one-page abstract and in a sense a condensation of the user's, operator's, and programmer's manual. Such a combination of documents should contain the essential information by the user along with any special notes by the operator and a listing by the programmer. A suggested outline for such documentation is given below.

1. Title and program library number
2. Author or authors involved in the program development
   a. Date issued or revised
3. Definition of the problem and scope of program
4. Theory and computational approach used
   a. Equations and numeric technique
   b. Modification made to facilitate programming
   c. Accuracy of computations made
   d. Sign conventions
5. Design philosophy
   a. Assumptions made
   b. Code sections included and omitted
   c. Specific computations
   d. Units
   e. Description of computational steps
6. Program restrictions and limitations
7. Description of applicable problems
8. Maximum size of problem
9. Data-preparation requirements
10. Input-data format
11. Interpretation of computer output
12. Illustrative examples

Documentation for most in-house programs is normally sufficient if it contains the information shown above. For a few sophisticated "systems" type programs, it will be necessary to have all five of the documented items listed previously. The interested reader is referred to the documentation standards for Type I and Type II programs of the IBM Corporation for good examples of this level of documentation.

2.8   Cataloging of Program Library

A reasonable means of cataloging the program, its documentation, the source and object decks, and a method of reference should be established. The number that is assigned to the program will be used in allocating computer and development costs, and for filing of documentation and card decks as well as for identification in a listing of library programs.

The list of programs in the library should be maintained and issued to the design staff periodically to keep them informed on the computer applications available for their use. This program listing should be accompanied by a one-page abstract describing the program application.

A program library usually consists of three basic types of programs, the programming and operating systems and subroutines, mathematical routines, and applications. Examples of program classification shown in Fig. 2.10 are patterned after the IBM 1620 Library Program Classifications.

1.0 Programming Systems and Subroutines
    1.1 Compiler and Assembly Programs
    1.2 Loading
    1.3 Punching
    1.4 Diagnostic
    1.5 Listing
    1.6 Miscellaneous General Purpose
    1.7 Supervisory Systems
2.0 Interpretive Programs
3.0 Mathematic Functions
4.0 Differential and Integral Equations
5.0 Matrix Programs
6.0 Statistical Programs
7.0 Mathematical Routines
8.0 Physical Sciences
9.0 Engineering Applications
    9.1 Aeronautical
    9.2 Civil
    9.3 Chemical
    9.4 Electrical
    9.5 Mechanical
    9.6 Petroleum
    9.7 Structural
    9.8 Nuclear
    9.9 Architectural
10.0 Management Science
    10.1 Linear Programming
    10.2 Simulations
    10.3 Resource Allocation and Scheduling
    10.4 Numerical Control
    10.5 Accounting
    10.6 Specifications
    10.7 Estimating
    10.8 Personnel
11.0 Economics

Fig. 2.10   Program classifications

A sample listing of the program library arranged according to the classifications indicated in Fig. 2.10 is illustrated in Fig. 2.11.

In addition to the program name the computing system for which the program is written is indicated, i.e., IBM 1130, IBM 7094, etc., the program number consists of six digits. The first two denote the major program classification. The next single digit represents the subdivision classification, and the last three digits denote the chronological sequence.

A one-digit code indicating the status of the program is given.

"1" denotes the program is currently in operation and available for immediate use.

"2" denotes the program is obsolete or has been superseded and will not appear on subsequent issues of the program library listing.

SARGENT AND LUNDY'S LIBRARY OF COMPUTER PROGRAMS AS OF AUG. 31, 1967
LISTING ACCORDING TO PROGRAM CLASSIFICATIONS

ACQ NO. PROGRAM NAME	SYS.	PROG.NO.	ST
1.0 PROGRAMMING SYSTEMS + SUBROUTINES			
1.1 COMPILER + ASSEMBLY PROGRAMS			
66 1130 DISK MONITOR SYSTEM	1130	01.1.001	1
1.2 LOADING			
1.3 PUNCHING			
111 REPRO (CARD REPRODUCING ROUTINE)	1130	01.3.001	1
1.4 DIAGNOSTIC			
1.5 LISTING			
96 LIST 1(ZAP)	1130	01.5.001	1
1.6 MISCELLANEOUS GENERAL PURPOSE			
1.7 SUPERVISORY SYSTEMS			
49 STRUCTURAL EXECUTIVE SYSTEM	1130	01.7.001	1
2.0 INTERPRETIVE PROGRAMS			
3.0 MATHEMATIC FUNCTIONS			
4.0 DIFFERENTIAL + INTEGRAL EQUATIONS			
5.0 MATRIX PROGRAMS			
94 SOLUTION OF SIMULTANEOUS EQUATIONS- 40X40 LIMIT	1130	05.0.001	1
6.0 STATISTICAL PROGRAMS			
7.0 MATHEMATICAL ROUTINES			
95 POLYNOMIAL CURVE FITTING	1130	07.0.001	
8.0 PHYSICAL SCIENCES			
9.0 ENGINEERING APPLICATIONS			
9.1 AERONAUTICAL			
9.2 CIVIL			
79 NATURAL + FORCED EVAPORATION OF COOLING LAKES	1130	09.2.006	3
86 1130 COGO (CIVIL ENGINEERING COORDINATE GEOMETRY)	1130	09.2.007	1
91 BACKWATER CURVES	1130	09.2.008	1
9.3 CHEMICAL			
9.4 ELECTRICAL			
9.5 MECHANICAL			
9.6 PETROLEUM			
9.7 STRUCTURAL			
30 PLATE GIRDER DESIGN - AISC CODE 1963	7094	09.7.015	1
31 STRESS (STRUCTURAL ENGINEERING SYSTEM SOLVER)	7094	09.7.016	1
40 FRAM (FRAMED STRUCTURES ANALYSIS PROG.)	7094	09.7.018	1
50 BEAM EDIT	1130	09.7.020	1
51 BEAM SELECTION	1130	09.7.021	1
52 COMPOSITE BEAM	1130	09.7.022	1
53 DEFLECTION	1130	09.7.023	3
76 1130 STRESS	1130	09.7.029	1
97 COMPRESSION MEMBER DESIGN	1130	09.7.031	3

Fig. 2.11   Sample program library listing

"3" denotes the program is in one of the many stages of development or validation.

2.9   Operating Procedure

The successful computer installation has well-defined operating policies and procedures to which the users adhere. The operations section is responsible for and operates the computer and peripheral equipment to process the data so that the computer system is effectively and efficiently used. They also schedule the work so as to keep turnaround time to a minimum.

The operations section must keep and maintain proper records of all transactions taking place in a given period. These records provide management with information on computer usage for accounting purposes, for performance monitoring, and for equipment evaluation.

At this point, it should be mentioned again that even the smallest office will have, conceptually at least, some kind of operating procedure. Larger offices may have need of a somewhat more formal procedure such as that presented below. In both cases, however, many of the concepts and record-keeping tools are valid.

When work is submitted to the operations section for processing it should be accompanied by some vehicle that will

1. Initiate computer services

2. Provide information from which management reports may be generated

3. Contain instructions to the operator for processing the job.

An example of such a vehicle is the request for computer service form shown in Fig. 2.12.

The information contained on the upper portion of this form will be keypunched onto a card, and from this unit record many different types of reports may be generated. This will provide management with information from which records and statistics can be compiled. From these reports the billing for computer usage can be made and the charge for the computer equipment reconciled and distributed. This aspect will be discussed further in the next section.

The lower portions of the form contain the instructions for keypunching, the program to be used, and operation of the computer as well as the type of input and the form of output desired.

A space at the bottom of the form provides for an authorized signature which initiates the processing of the work through the operations section.

The information required for this form is furnished by the user when submitting his work to the operation section. In order to maintain proper records no work should be accepted without this form.

The mechanics of the operating procedure in processing the work is shown diagrammatically in Fig. 2.13.

The scheduler upon receipt of the work and the request form punches the time the work was submitted on the form. All work is processed in a sequence designated by the date and time received. This time is used for establishing priority and precedence in scheduling the work.

The scheduler then arranges for keypunching of the data and reserves time for processing on the computer in-house or at a service bureau. To aid in reserving time on the in-house computer a time log is kept as shown in Fig. 2.14.

From the estimated running time on the request form the scheduler

SARGENT & LUNDY
ENGINEERS
CHICAGO

REQUEST FOR COMPUTER SERVICES

NAME	INITIALS(1-3)	EXT. NO.	ROOM NO.	DATE SUB. (4-8)	TIME SUB.

DEPARTMENT			DEPT. CODE (9-10)	DATE REQ.	TIME REQ.

STATION, PROJECT, OR CONTRACT NAME (11-24)	JOB. NO. (25-30)

PROGRAM NAME (31-42)	PROGRAM NO. (43-50)	EST. RUNNING TIME

MACHINE	( ) KEYPUNCH ( ) SORT ( ) LIST ( ) COMPUTER(SPECIFY)	MACH. CODE (51-52)	(53) ( ) PRODUCTION ( ) DEVELOPMENT	ACTUAL RUNNING TIME (54-58)

TYPE OF JOB(60-61)
1( ) FORTRAN COMPILATION   4( ) VALIDATION
2( ) ASSY. LANGUAGE COMPILATION   5( ) TRAINING
3( ) PROGRAM TESTING AND DEBUGGING 6( ) RESEARCH
                                  7( ) OTHER

KEYPUNCH

NUMBER OF CARDS (62-65)	NUMBER OF FORMS (66-68)

INPUT

CARDS:

DISK:

TAPE:

TYPE OF CARDS:

( ) BLUE EDGE   ( ) SOLID BLUE
( ) GREEN EDGE   ( ) SOLID GREEN
( ) RED EDGE   ( ) SOLID RED
( ) YELLOW EDGE   ( ) SOLID YELLOW
( ) WHITE   ( ) FORTRAN

INSTRUCTIONS:

( ) ACCORDING TO INSTRUCTIONS ON FORMS
( ) PUNCH ONLY AS SHOWN
( ) STRESS
( ) FORTRAN
( ) OTHER-PLEASE STATE CLEARLY

OUTPUT

CARDS:

DISK:

TAPE:

PRINTER:
( ) LARGE SIZE   ____ PLY PAPER
( ) SMALL SIZE
( ) OTHER (SPECIFY)

OPERATING INSTRUCTIONS:

REMARKS(69-79)

APPROVED BY _____

Fig. 2.12   Request for computer service

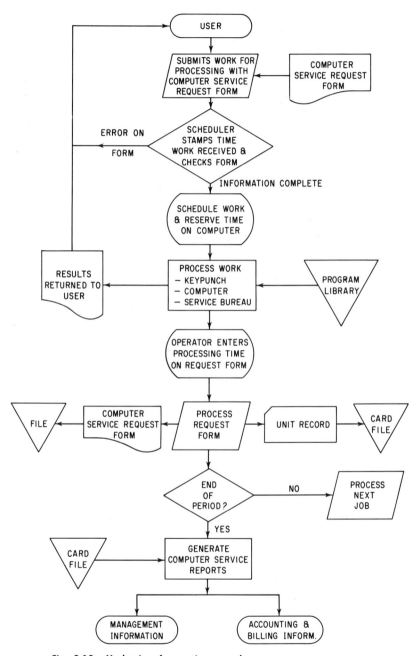

Fig. 2.13 Mechanics of operating procedure

SARGENT & LUNDY ENGINEERS
IBM 1130 Computing System

Day:	Date:	
Time	Time	Time
0800	1200	1600
0805	1205	1605
0810	1210	1610
0815	1215	1615
0820	1220	1620
0825	1225	1625
0830	1230	1630
0835	1235	1635
0840	1240	1640
0845	1245	1645
0850	1250	1650
0855	1255	1655
0900	1300	1700
0905	1305	1705
0910	1310	1710
0915	1315	1715
0920	1320	1720
0925	1325	1725
0930	1330	1730
0935	1335	1735
0940	1340	1740
0945	1345	1745
0950	1350	1750
0955	1355	1755
1000	1400	1800
1005	1405	1805
1010	1410	1810
1015	1415	1815
1020	1420	1820
1025	1425	1825
1030	1430	1830
1035	1435	1835
1040	1440	1840
1045	1445	1845
1050	1450	1850
1055	1455	1855
1100	1500	1900
1105	1505	1905
1110	1510	1910
1115	1515	1915
1120	1520	1920
1125	1525	1925
1130	1530	1930
1135	1535	1935
1140	1540	1940
1145	1545	1945
1150	1550	1950
1155	1555	1955

Fig. 2.14   Computer time log

blocks out the time required as it is available. Any conflicts are resolved by the head of the section or division. Scheduling time at a service bureau will depend on the regulations of that installation and the availability of time.

When the work has been keypunched, the scheduler proceeds to arrange the work for processing by the computer. The cards are assembled and arranged according to the operating instructions for that program. The object deck is obtained from the program library. To initiate the processing and the work the scheduler punches the starting time on the request form. At the completion of the job he punches the time the job ended and enters the difference onto the request form as actual running time.

The program object decks are returned to the library file and the data cards and results are returned to the user. The cycle from the time the job was submitted until the results are returned to the user is "turnaround" time. This time is most critical and must be minimized for an efficient operation.

At the conclusion of a period the records of all the transactions that have taken place during the period are processed to produce various computer service reports for management information and accounting purposes.

The reports which can be generated from the data obtained from the computer service request forms are:

1. A chronological listing (by department) of all transactions made—keypunching and computer usage

2. A departmental summary of the production work performed

3. A departmental summary of development work performed

4. A company total of all production work performed

5. A company total of all development work performed

6. Computer time and manpower expended for program development.

Illustrative examples of the various types of computer-usage reports are given in Figs. 2.15 to 2.20.

2.10 Economics of
Computer Utilization

Many factors must be considered in the economics of justifying an in-house computer installation. Many benefits, both tangible and intangible, occur through the use of computers. However, one cannot justify the economics of an installation solely on intangible benefits.

Tangible benefits result from the savings in design man-hours and the ability to handle an increased work load with the same staff. Intangible benefits accrue from being able to extend the engineer's capability to

SARGENT + LUNDY
ENGINEERS
CHICAGO

COMPUTER SERVICES COSTS FOR EACH MACHINE - PRODUCTION AND DEVELOPMENT - MAY 1967

DEPARTMENT - STRUCTURAL

INITIALS OF SUBMITTER	DATE SUB	STATION PROJECT OR CONTRACT	JOB NUMBER	PROGRAM TITLE	PROGRAM NUMBER	JOB TYPE	MACHINE	ACT RUN TIME	NO CARDS	NO FORMS	REMARKS
JF	25	BALDWIN	3682	STAND	1.7.001	P-0	IBM 1130	234.60	0	0	COMP. BEAMS
JG	25	BALDWIN	3682		20.0.000	P-0	IBM 1130	12.00	0	0	
AL	25	BALDWIN	3682	GIRDER	9.7.015	P-0	IBM 7094	1.75	0	0	R59N
AL	25	BALDWIN	3682	GIRDER	9.7.015	P-0	IBM 7094	1.38	0	0	U96N
AL	25	BALDWIN	3682	GIRDER	9.7.015	P-0	HWL 200	1.47	0	0	
AL	25	BALDWIN	3682	GIRDER	9.7.015	P-0	HWL 200	1.50	6	1	
JMM	25	CE 516	0	CE 516	0.0.000	D-0	KEYPUNCH	0.00	68	5	
MD	26	FT. ST. VRAIN	3614-1	COGO	20.0.000	D-0	KEYPUNCH	0.00	0	0	
JF	26	BALDWIN	3682	GIRDER	9.2.006	P-0	IBM 1130	13.20	0	0	T45N
AL	26	BALDWIN	3682	GIRDER	9.7.015	P-7	IBM 7094	1.98	0	0	T46N
AL	26	BALDWIN	3682	GIRDER	9.7.015	P-0	HWL 200	2.52	0	0	
JMM	26	CE516	0	CE516	9.7.015	P-7	IBM 7094	1.57	0	0	LISTING
GLP	26	RIVER ROUGE	3549	STRESS	9.7.015	P-0	HWL 200	1.50	0	0	
GLP	26	RIVER ROUGE	3549	STRESS	20.0.000	D-0	IBM 1130	80.40	0	0	
AS	26	EDGEWATER	3582	COGO	9.7.029	P-0	IBM 1130	7.80	0	0	
KCC	27	CAYUGA	3689	GIRDER	9.7.029	P-0	KEYPUNCH	0.00	594	21	
KCC	27	CAYUGA	3689	GIRDER	9.2.006	P-0	IBM 1130	10.80	0	0	U50N
MD	27	FT. ST. VRAIN	3614-1	COGO	9.7.015	P-0	IBM 7094	1.07	0	0	
AS	27	EDGEWATER	3582	COGO	9.2.006	P-0	HWL 200	0.41	0	0	
JF	29	BALDWIN	3682	GIRDER	9.2.006	P-0	IBM 1130	41.40	0	0	V50N
JF	29	BALDWIN	3682	GIRDER	9.7.015	P-0	IBM 1130	6.60	0	0	
JFH	29	CAYUGA	3689	BACKWATER	9.7.015	P-0	IBM 7094	1.79	0	0	
JFM	29	BALDWIN	3682	FRAN	9.2.008	P-0	HWL 200	2.52	0	0	
JFM	29	BALDWIN	3682	FRAN	9.7.018	P-0	IBM 1130	132.00	0	0	
GLP	29	RIVER ROUGE	3549	STRESS	9.7.018	P-0	IBM 1130	6.00	0	0	
LE	30	QUAD CITIES	3620	STRESS	9.7.016	P-0	KEYPUNCH	0.00	237	19	
LE	30	QUAD CITIES	3620	STRESS	9.7.029	P-0	IBM 1130	34.20	116	4	
MD	31	FT. ST. VRAIN	3614-1	COGO	0.0.000	P-0	KEYPUNCH	0.00	87	1	
MD	31	FT. ST. VRAIN	3614-1	COGO	9.2.006	P-0	KEYPUNCH	0.00	146	8	
TD	31	CAYUGA	3689	PLATEG RDER	9.2.006	P-0	IBM 1130	24.00	0	0	
TD	31	CAYUGA	3689	PLATEG RDER	9.7.015	P-0	IBM 7094	1.31	0	0	X35N
JF	31	BALDWIN	3682	STAND	9.7.015	P-0	HWL 200	0.30	0	0	
					1.7.001	P-0	KEYPUNCH	0.00	344	24	

Fig. 2.15 Chronological list of all transactions

SARGENT + LUNDY
ENGINEERS
CHICAGO

COMPUTER SERVICES COSTS FOR EACH MACHINE – PRODUCTION AND DEVELOPMENT – MAY 1967

DEPARTMENT – STRUCTURAL

COST SUMMARY
PRODUCTION

JOB NUMBER	IBM 1440	HWL 200	IITRI IBM 7094	MAC IBM 7094		IBM 1130	OTHER COMP	STC 360	STC 1401	KEY PUNCH	TOTAL COST
3334	0.00	0.00	0.00	0.00	0.00	33.00	0.00	0.00	0.00	0	27.50
3416-1	0.00	0.00	0.00	0.00	0.00	0.00	0.00	0.00	0.00	19	1.44
3447	0.00	5.70	2.01	0.00	0.00	327.00	0.00	0.00	0.00	592	343.85
3549	0.00	2.12	1.31	0.00	0.00	7.80	0.00	0.00	0.00	710	75.57
3582	0.00	0.00	0.00	0.00	0.00	88.19	0.00	0.00	0.00	305	96.57
3595-1	0.00	0.83	1.21	0.00	0.00	284.40	0.00	0.00	0.00	40	253.10
3605	0.00	8.22	8.26	0.73	0.00	69.00	0.00	0.00	0.00	248	176.20
3605-1	0.00	0.07	1.41	0.00	0.00	0.00	0.00	0.00	0.00	0	14.18
3614-1	0.00	0.00	0.00	0.00	0.00	518.99	0.00	0.00	0.00	1339	533.43
3614-2	0.00	0.00	0.00	0.00	0.00	10.80	0.00	0.00	0.00	60	13.54
3614-3	0.00	0.00	0.00	0.00	0.00	164.39	0.00	0.00	0.00	558	179.14
3620	0.00	43.82	23.78	13.80	0.00	670.79	0.00	0.00	0.00	5586	1412.00
3663	0.00	18.75	39.47	0.00	0.00	0.00	0.00	0.00	0.00	0	416.58
3682	0.00	37.09	33.03	0.00	0.00	1012.79	0.00	0.00	0.00	3052	1448.09
3689	0.00	15.28	14.83	0.00	0.00	1000.19	0.00	0.00	0.00	1447	1109.25
3773	0.00	0.00	0.00	0.00	0.00	132.60	0.00	0.00	0.00	17	111.79
TIME(MIN)	0.00	131.91	125.34	14.53	0.00	4319.99	0.00	0.00	0.00	13973	
RATE/HR	50.00	70.00	600.00	625.00	0.00	50.00	0.00	0.00	75.00	0.07	
COST	0.00	153.93	1253.49	151.35	0.00	3600.00	0.00	0.00	0.00	1053.48	6212.23

Fig. 2.16 Summary of production work by job

SARGENT + LUNDY
ENGINEERS
CHICAGO

COMPUTER SERVICES COSTS FOR EACH MACHINE – PRODUCTION AND DEVELOPMENT – MAY 1967

DEPARTMENT – STRUCTURAL

COST SUMMARY
DEVELOPMENT

PROGRAM NUMBER	IBM 1440	HWL 200	IITRI IBM 7094	MAC IBM 7094	IBM 704	IBM 1130	OTHER COMP	LISTING	SORTING	KEY PUNCH	TOTAL COST
1.7.001	0.00	0.00	0.00	0.00	0.00	0.00	0.00	0.00	0.00	140	10.58
9.7.029	0.00	0.00	0.00	0.00	0.00	21.60	0.00	0.00	0.00	0	18.00
10.8.001	0.00	0.00	0.00	0.00	0.00	30.60	0.00	0.00	0.00	0	25.50
20.0.000	0.00	0.00	0.00	0.00	0.00	223.79	0.00	0.00	0.00	956	258.77
TIME(MIN)	0.00	0.00	0.00	0.00	0.00	275.99	0.00	0.00	0.00	1096	
RATE/HR	50.00	70.00	600.00	625.00	0.00	50.00		75.00	19.50	0.075	
COST	0.00	0.00	0.00	0.00	0.00	230.00	0.00	0.00	0.00	82.85	312.85

Fig. 2.17 Summary of development work performed by program number

SARGENT + LUNDY
ENGINEERS
CHICAGO

COMPUTER SERVICES COSTS FOR EACH MACHINE - PRODUCTION AND DEVELOPMENT - MAY 1967

GRAND TOTALS
PRODUCTION

JOB NUMBER	IBM 1440	HWL 200	IITRI IBM 7094	MAC IBM 7094		IBM 1130	OTHER COMP	STC 360	STC 1401	KEY PUNCH	TOTAL COST
2340	0.00	0.00	0.00	0.00	0.00	2144.53	0.00	0.00	0.00	0	1787.11
3079	63.60	0.00	0.00	0.00	0.00	0.00	0.00	0.00	0.00	179	66.75
3218	0.00	0.00	0.00	0.00	0.00	208.19	0.00	0.00	0.00	21	175.08
3323	0.00	0.00	0.00	0.00	0.00	25.80	0.00	0.00	0.00	0	21.50
3325	0.00	7.36	30.59	4.76	0.00	5.40	0.00	0.00	0.00	0	368.66
3334	0.00	0.00	0.00	0.00	0.00	33.00	0.00	0.00	0.00	71	32.89
3416-1	0.00	0.00	0.00	0.00	0.00	0.00	0.00	0.00	0.00	19	1.44
3417	45.00	0.00	0.00	0.00	0.00	0.00	0.00	0.00	0.00	0	37.50
3447	0.00	5.70	2.01	0.00	0.00	730.19	0.00	0.00	0.00	1542	751.55
3498	0.00	0.00	0.00	0.00	0.00	28.80	0.00	0.00	0.00	56	28.24
3549	0.00	2.12	1.31	0.00	0.00	7.80	0.00	0.00	0.00	710	75.57
3567	0.00	0.00	0.00	0.00	0.00	241.79	0.00	0.00	0.00	151	212.93
3582	0.00	0.00	0.00	0.00	0.00	399.59	0.00	0.00	0.00	780	392.06
3595-1	0.00	0.83	1.21	0.00	0.00	284.40	0.00	0.00	0.00	40	253.10
3595-2	0.00	5.75	29.81	0.00	0.00	151.19	0.00	0.00	0.00	773	489.68
3605	0.00	8.22	8.26	0.73	0.00	69.00	0.00	0.00	0.00	433	190.17
3605-1	0.00	0.07	1.41	0.00	0.00	0.00	0.00	0.00	0.00	0	14.18
3668	0.00	0.00	0.00	0.00	0.00	0.00	0.00	0.00	0.00	27	2.05
3682	0.00	42.48	56.59	0.00	0.00	1037.39	0.00	0.00	0.00	3380	1735.08
3687	39.00	0.00	0.00	0.00	0.00	0.00	0.00	0.00	0.00	372	60.90
3689	0.00	15.28	14.83	0.00	0.00	1279.19	0.00	0.00	0.00	1836	1371.66
3690	0.00	0.68	3.02	0.00	0.00	0.00	0.00	0.00	0.00	0	30.99
3708	0.00	0.00	0.00	0.00	0.00	113.39	0.00	0.00	0.00	281	115.75
3710	0.00	68.78	15.52	0.00	0.00	391.79	0.00	0.00	0.00	736	617.50
3723	0.00	0.00	0.00	0.00	0.00	59.39	0.00	0.00	0.00	0	49.50
3773	0.00	0.00	0.00	0.00	0.00	132.60	0.00	0.00	0.00	17	111.79
TIME(MIN)	147.60	223.07	241.26	40.69	0.00	9127.27	0.00	42.00	0.00	19901	
RATE/HR	50.00	70.00	600.00	625.00	0.00	50.00	75.00	19.50	0.07		
COST	123.00	260.25	2412.69	423.94	0.00	7607.12	0.00	52.50	0.00	1502.27	12380.63

Fig. 2.18   Total production usage

attain a higher level of engineering and greater use of his talents, thereby keeping abreast of the ever-changing technology.

An example cost structure for operating a computer installation is illustrated in Fig. 2.21.

The operating costs consist of two major components—computer and manpower. Computer costs include the monthly rental of hardware equipment, i.e., central processing unit, input-output units, keypunch, verifier, sorter, etc. Manpower costs include the salaries of analysts, programmers, and operating staff.

Production work is defined as that for which a computer program is used to augment the analysis and design on a specific project. The charges for the use of the computer and manpower can be made directly to that project or job.

Development work is defined as that required to study the feasibility of an application, prepare the problem specifications and flow charts, do the programming, test and debug a program, or validate existing program

SARGENT + LUNDY
ENGINEERS
CHICAGO

COMPUTER SERVICES COSTS FOR EACH MACHINE - PRODUCTION AND DEVELOPMENT - MAY 1967

GRAND TOTALS
DEVELOPMENT

PROGRAM NUMBER	IBM 1440	HWL 200	IITRI IBM 7094	MAC IBM 7094		IBM 1130	OTHER COMP 0.00	STC 360	STC 1401	KEY PUNCH	TOTAL COST
1.1.001	0.00	0.00	0.00	0.00	0.00	48.00	0.00	0.00	0.00	0	40.00
1.6.001	0.00	0.00	0.00	0.00	0.00	138.00	0.00	0.00	0.00	0	115.00
1.7.001	0.00	0.00	27.89	0.00	0.00	9.60	0.00	0.00	0.00	140	18.58
9.2.005	0.00	18.38	0.00	0.00	0.00	24.00	0.00	0.00	0.00	0	320.34
9.2.008	0.00	0.00	0.00	0.00	0.00	116.99	0.00	0.00	0.00	30	99.77
9.4.012	0.00	0.00	0.00	0.00	0.00	70.80	0.00	0.00	0.00	74	64.61
9.4.021	0.00	0.00	0.00	0.00	0.00	158.39	0.00	0.00	0.00	0	132.00
9.4.023	0.00	0.00	0.00	0.00	0.00	28.20	0.00	0.00	0.00	0	23.50
9.4.024	0.00	0.00	0.00	0.00	0.00	19.80	0.00	0.00	0.00	159	28.54
9.4.025	0.00	0.00	0.00	0.00	0.00	254.39	0.00	0.00	0.00	99	219.49
9.5.005	0.00	0.00	0.00	0.00	0.00	208.79	0.00	0.00	0.00	230	191.32
9.5.010	0.00	0.00	0.00	0.00	0.00	3.00	0.00	0.00	0.00	0	2.50
9.7.021	0.00	0.00	0.00	0.00	0.00	46.79	0.00	0.00	0.00	0	39.00
9.7.022	0.00	0.00	0.00	0.00	0.00	38.40	0.00	0.00	0.00	0	32.00
9.7.029	0.00	0.00	0.00	0.00	0.00	113.99	0.00	0.00	0.00	31	97.34
9.7.030	0.00	60.62	16.79	0.00	0.00	0.00	0.00	0.00	0.00	578	282.28
10.3.003	4.20	0.00	0.00	0.00	0.00	0.00	0.00	0.00	0.00	0	3.50
10.3.004	0.00	0.00	0.00	0.00	0.00	624.00	0.00	0.00	0.00	794	579.90
10.5.001	0.00	0.00	0.00	0.00	0.00	161.39	0.00	0.00	0.00	0	134.50
10.8.001	0.00	0.00	0.00	0.00	0.00	269.39	0.00	0.00	0.00	307	247.67
10.9.001	0.00	0.00	0.00	0.00	0.00	31.20	0.00	0.00	0.00	0	26.00
11.1.006	0.00	0.00	0.00	0.00	0.00	40.20	0.00	0.00	0.00	90	49.29
11.1.007	0.00	0.00	0.00	0.00	0.00	90.00	0.00	0.00	0.00	0	75.00
20.0.000	0.00	0.00	0.00	0.00	0.00	610.19	0.00	0.00	0.00	1149	595.38
TIME(MIN)	4.20	79.00	44.68	0.00	0.00	3105.39	0.00	0.00	0.00	3681	
RATE/HR	50.00	70.00	600.00	625.00	0.00	50.00	75.00	19.50	0.07		
COST	3.50	92.21	446.89	0.00	0.00	2588.00	0.00	0.00	0.00	277.91	3408.52

Fig. 2.19 Total development work performed

obtained from a library source. Charges for this effort are made directly to the program.

Development work is further divided into that which is done to develop program applications for the firm's own in-house use, such as feasibility studies, payroll and accounting applications, and project-management scheduling, and that work required to develop applications for a general library. Development work which is done to build a professional library of computer applications is that effort expended for research and programming of design problems which benefit the client by reducing material costs and design man-hours.

These categories are the major functions in the cost structure of a computer installation. How these costs are distributed and how the development and programming costs are recovered is a matter of company policy. The computer is still too new to have a standard method or procedure established. There are as many ways to distribute and recover these costs as there are accounting methods and company policies.

SARGENT + LUNDY
ENGINEERS
CHICAGO

PROGRAM DEVELOPMENT TIME - DEC 1966

PROGRAM TITLE	PROGRAM NUMBER	COMP LAST MONTH	TIME TOT TO 1ST OF MONTH	THIS PER	PROGRAMMING TIME TOT TO END OF PER	PER CENT COMPLETE FEA STY	NUM ANA	FLOW CHART SYS	FLOW CHART PRG	COD	DBG	WRT UP	DATE OF COMPLETION STARTED	PLACED INTO PROD	COMPL EXC WRT FOR UP
STAIR	9.7.014	0.00	0.00	0.0	0.0	0	0	0	0	0	0	0	JAN-64	APR-64	-
PLATE GIRDER	9.7.015	0.00	0.00	0.0	0.0	0	0	0	0	0	0	0	-	-	-
STRESS	9.7.016	0.00	0.00	0.0	0.0	0	0	0	0	0	0	0	-	-	-
JPL	9.7.017	0.00	0.00	0.0	0.0	0	0	0	0	0	0	0	-	-	-
FRAN	9.7.018	0.00	0.00	0.0	0.0	0	0	0	0	0	0	0	-	-	-
TEMP GRD	9.7.019	0.00	0.00	0.0	0.0	0	0	0	0	0	0	0	-	-	-
BEAM EDIT	9.7.020	0.00	7.21	0.0	0.0	0	0	0	0	0	0	0	MAY-65	-	-
BEAM SELTN	9.7.021	0.00	8.26	0.0	0.0	0	0	0	0	0	0	0	MAY-65	-	-
COMP BEAM	9.7.022	0.00	0.00	0.0	0.0	0	0	0	0	0	0	0	MAY-65	-	-
DEFLECTION	9.7.023	0.00	0.00	0.0	0.0	0	0	0	0	0	0	0	MAY-65	-	-
MOM SHR DGM	9.7.024	0.00	0.00	0.0	0.0	0	0	0	0	0	0	0	-	-	-
TIGER II	9.8.001	0.00	0.00	0.0	0.0	0	0	0	0	0	0	0	-	-	-
REACTOR SIT	9.8.001	0.00	0.00	0.0	0.0	0	0	0	0	0	0	0	-	-	-
LEAST COST	10.3.001	0.00	0.00	0.0	0.0	0	0	0	0	0	0	0	-	-	-
DATING CPN	10.3.002	0.00	0.00	0.0	0.0	0	0	0	0	0	0	0	-	-	-
BIM PAYROLL	10.5.001	0.00	0.00	0.0	0.0	0	0	0	0	0	0	0	APR -65	-	-
COMP. SER. RPT	10.9.001	0.00	12.27	0.0	0.0	0	0	0	0	0	0	0	SEPT-65	-	-
OTHER	20.0.000	0.00	0.00	0.0	0.0	0	0	0	0	0	0	0	-	-	-
TOTALS				0.0	18040.0										

Fig. 2.20 Summary of program development time

2.11 Conclusions

Developing a computer capability requires the integrated efforts of management and programmers, a library of applications, and the availability of computer facilities. It also requires an environment in which all these factors contribute and interact. The most important element is design talent—people with imagination and initiative to apply these tools to the solution of design problems. At this point in time there is no longer any excuse for not having access or availability to computer facilities. These facilities are readily available at the local service bureaus, or a firm can

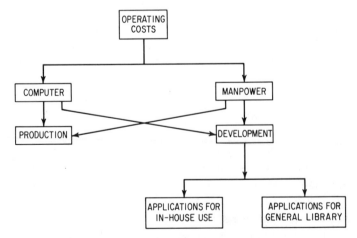

Fig. 2.21 Computer installation cost structure

have either a remote teletypewriter console for time-sharing to larger computer systems or a small-scale computer system.

Many people feel that the primary purpose of computers is just to save design time, which it does, but it has an even greater purpose and that is to extend the designer's capability to obtain a higher level and greater use of his talent.

With the aid of a computer man is able to solve some of the complex problems which confront the profession and can keep pace with today's vastly accelerated technology that has been brought about, in part, by the computer.

REFERENCES

1. "Computer Usage in the Manufacturing Industry," *Business Automation,* vol. 13, no. 10, p. 53, October, 1966.
2. "Occupations in Electronic Computing Systems," U.S. Department of Labor, Manpower Administration, Bureau of Employment Security, Washington, D.C., July, 1965.
3. *Salary Survey Report for Data Processing Positions,* Phillip H. Weber & Associates, Inc., 120 South LaSalle Street, Chicago, Ill. 60603.
4. "Data Processing Personnel Handbook," *1966 Special Report from Computer and Automation,* Berkely Enterprises, Inc., 815 Washington Street, Newtonville, Mass.
5. Gene Bylinsky, "Help Wanted 50,000 Programmers," *Fortune,* vol. LXXV, no. 3, p. 141, March, 1967.
6. "The Software Snarl," *Time,* vol. 90, no. 7, p. 75, August, 1967.
7. IBM Aptitude Test for *Programmer Personnel Manual* R29-0025, *Manual for Administrating and Scoring ATPP* R29-0026, IBM Data Processing Division, 112 East Post Road, White Plains, N.Y. 10601.
8. "EXECUTIVE Compensation Service," *Administrative & Technical Positions Report,* American Management Association, 135 West 50th Street, New York, N.Y.
9. "Use of Computers in Structural Analysis," Department of Building and Safety, Engineering Research and Development Bureau, City of Los Angeles, Calif.

CHAPTER THREE *Engineering*

Applications

By G. Neil Harper

The engineering applications of computers in design offices reflect a very broad spectrum of disciplines and degrees of sophistication. Several examples of operational programs have been selected from the structural, mechanical, electrical, and architectural engineering disciplines to illustrate both the broad range of current applications and a typical level of computer sophistication. An example of recent developments in structural engineering is discussed to illustrate what may well be the next level of sophistication in engineering applications.

3.1 Definition of Scope

Engineering applications of computers imply such a vast scale of technical activity that it is completely unreasonable to consider treating the general field. Accordingly, this general topic must be delimited by the blanket exclusion of many fascinating applications in engineering disciplines that are only marginally related to engineering as it applies to the building industry.

Even within this relatively narrow spectrum of engineering, the actual number of computer applications is quite large, and the applications range over the diverse disciplines of structural, mechanical, electrical, and architectural engineering. It is therefore apparent that any comprehensive treatment of such broad fields in which computer applications are growing at an exponential rate is also out of the question.

With these considerations in mind, a limited selection of representative examples of computer applications has been included in this chapter. Such a plan provides selection from different disciplines and at the same time depth of treatment for the examples chosen.

The first part of the chapter will deal with what might be called traditional applications that have been typical of office practice. The second part focuses on a problem-oriented language that is being developed and used in structural engineering and that will undoubtedly have significant influence on the development of applications in other engineering disciplines.

3.2 Structural Engineering

The structural-engineering profession has enjoyed a relatively long acquaintance with computer applications. As early as the mid-fifties, some of the first programs were being developed, mainly in universities and larger engineering firms. By and large, the major programs developed during this time were analysis programs for handling portions of problems, such as moment distribution for continuous beams, truss analysis, and small-rigid-frame analysis. Early investigation of matrix techniques was also beginning.

By the early sixties, the so-called second-generation computers were beginning to come on the market, with their increased speeds and memory sizes. The applications began to grow rapidly in number and size. Larger-scale programs which utilized matrix methods and other techniques for solving the large sets of equations that analysis programs typically produce were becoming more common. Some early work in elementary design of structural members, optimization, finite elements, structural dynamics, and topological formulations is also reported in the literature.[1,2,3] By and large, however, the grass roots of the practicing profession had been touched only at several larger, more advanced firms.

Also during these early 1960s, the first developments in problem-oriented languages (POLs) began to appear on the scene. COGO (for Coordinate Geometry), was developed at M.I.T. by Prof. C. L. Miller and his colleagues as the prototype application. A language for structural engineers, STRESS (for Structural Engineering Systems Solver), was another major development of problem-oriented languages at M.I.T. With the introduction of the third-generation computers in the mid-sixties, the development of similar languages for other fields, and even of POLs to generate POLs, has become a rapidly evolving field. Such developments will undoubtedly be recorded as one of the most significant advances of the sixties in easing the burden of man-machine communication.

The arrival of third-generation computers not only has given impetus to new and more sophisticated applications on large machines but has also brought the small, inexpensive computer within the reach of an astonishingly large number of smaller professional offices. As a result, the structural application of computers is proceeding on two distinct levels. On the larger computers, major advances are being made in development of comprehensive systems for information processing of structural data. One of the most advanced of these systems, STRUDL (for Structural Design Language), is described in some detail later in this chapter. On the smaller computers, the practicing profession is making rapid strides in implementing programs which were first developed on a research basis in the late fifties and early sixties. Two examples of this type of application have been selected to show the general nature of current office practice.

The first such example is representative of a large number of programs likely to be found in the library of any structural computer installation. Figure 3.1 shows an idealized structural framing system for a single floor of a building that could be anywhere from two to a hundred stories tall. Such an idealized framing system is frequently used in both steel and

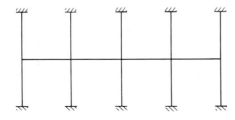

Fig. 3.1 Idealized rigid frame for moment distribution

concrete design for performing a moment distribution of gravity floor loads in order to size the major girders and to obtain gravity moments in columns.

MOMENT DISTRIBUTION OF
CONTINUOUS FRAMES

Scope

    This program will analyze continuous spans of a floor frame having columns above and/or below the span level. The program will also handle continuous beams with no columns. Columns can be either fixed or pinned at the far end. No correction is made for any sidesway effects.

Input

    Job Number
    Frame Identification
    Number of Column Lines
    Maximum Number of Distribution Cycles
    Span Number, Beam and Column Inertias and Lengths
    Loading Condition (Uniform and/or Concentrated Loads)

Output

    Echo Print of Input Data
    End Moments at Each End of Each Member
    Moments and Shears beneath Each Concentrated Load

Fig. 3.2   One-page abstract describing a moment-distribution program

A one-page abstract describing a moment-distribution program for this type of frame is shown in Fig. 3.2. The program reads in gravity loads, geometry, and estimated member inertias from cards which are punched from an input sheet of the form shown in Fig. 3.3. A moment distribution is performed and the resulting moments and shears are printed out as shown in Fig. 3.4.

Such a program is typical of many to be found in office practice in several respects. It treats an often recurring analysis problem in a straight-forward, efficient way, with some provision made for slightly varying input data (such as number of spans or number and types of loads). The program is small, specialized in scope, and requires only a modest programming effort. If the problem at hand had cantilevers on the spans or had significant sidesway, or if deflections along the members were to be computed, a similar special-purpose program would probably be used which would require much of the same input as the example problem.

For each such special-purpose program, an office is likely to maintain a small program description, similar to the one-page abstract shown in Fig. 3.2, along with input sheets (Fig. 3.3) and perhaps a description of results of an example problem (Fig. 3.4). Such documentation is vital if the programs are to be used over any period of time by several engineers.

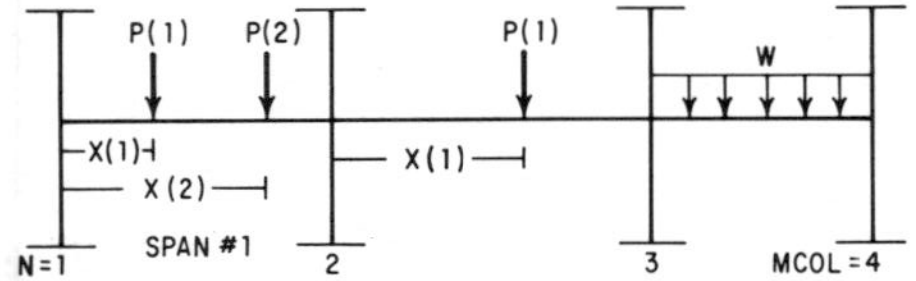

MOMENT DISTRIBUTION OF
CONTINUOUS FRAMES

N=1 SPAN #1 — MCOL = 4

HEADER CARD

ITEMS	JOB NO.	SPAN ID	MCOL	MCYC
UNITS				
FORMAT	F 7.3	F 5.2	I3	I3
CARD COLS.	1,0,2,0,2,0	2,0,0	4	1,0

DETAIL CARDS

TYPE 1	N	BEAM INERTIA	BEAM SPAN	COL. I BELOW	COL LENGTH BELOW	COL. I ABOVE	COL. LENGTH ABOVE
UNITS	–	IN⁴	FT	IN⁴	FT	IN⁴	FT
TYPE 2	N	W	P	X	P	X	P
UNITS	–	KIPS/FT	KIPS	FT	F5.0		
FORMAT	I5						
	1	1.0	2.0	.5	1.0	.4	.9
	1	1.0	3.0	1.0	1.0	.8	.9
	2	1.0		1.5			
	2	.8.5	1.0				
	3	1.0	2.0	1.0	1.0	.8	.9
	3	1	.5				
	4			.5	1.0	.4	.9
	4						

INSTRUCTIONS: LOCATION OF DECIMAL POINT IS INDICATED BY DOTTED LINE, ENTER DATA ACCORDINGLY

Fig. 3.3 Input sheet for moment distribution

60

MOM DISTRIB — UNIF MOM OF INERTIA — S102.02
JOB NO.= 102.02, SPAN= 2.00, COLS= 4, MAX CYCLES= 10

COL	B E A M INERTIA	SPAN	COL BELOW INERTIA	LENGTH	COL ABOVE INERTIA	LENGTH	UNIFORM LOAD–K/FT
1	1.00	20.00	5.00	10.00	4.00	9.00	1.00
2	10.00	30.00	10.00	10.00	8.00	9.00	0.85
3	10.00	20.00	10.00	10.00	8.00	9.00	1.00
4	0.00	0.00	5.00	10.00	4.00	9.00	0.00

COL NO	COL MOM BELOW	BEAM MOMENT	COL MOM ABOVE	SHEAR	LD DIST × PT		LOAD
1	22.72		20.20				
		−42.92		12.23	0.00	L	
		29.41		2.23	10.00	1	5.00
		−48.23		−12.76	20.00	R	
2	25.30		22.49				
		−96.03		17.64	0.00	L	
		73.09		4.89	15.00	1	10.00
		−99.03		−17.85	30.00	R	
3	−19.29		−17.15				
		−62.58		14.28	0.00	L	
		30.30		4.28	10.00	1	5.00
		−26.81		−10.71	20.00	R	
4	−14.19		−12.61				

CYCLES = 4

Fig. 3.4 **Output results from moment distribution**

Given this large fragmentation and duplication in small analysis programs, there has been a natural desire to integrate the programs into a more comprehensive general-purpose system. This has become particularly true as bulk storage facilities have become available on the smaller computers found in the engineering office. The data-structuring and -handling problems for such an integrated system are, however, by no means insignificant. An effective solution to the problem will undoubtedly require a new look at systems-programming techniques now being developed. To date, however, any interfacing or integration of the small special-purpose programs, at least on the moderate-sized computers found in most offices, has been done only in certain specialized circumstances.

The second structural application example is also a program very likely to be found in any structural computer installation. Column design, in this case steel-column design, is a very time-consuming task in the design of any building frame. Figure 3.5 shows a one-page abstract for a program that will design steel columns subject to combined axial loads and bending about two axes for a variety of gravity, temperature, and wind loads. Given the column mark, loading conditions, and certain stability factors like K, CM, and length H, the program will cycle through a table of rolled shapes to select a section which satisfies all the requirements for combined stresses of the AISC code, for the worst of the given loading conditions.

STEEL-COLUMN DESIGN

Scope

For a given load, unbraced length, end restraint and yield strength of steel, the lightest member which satisfies the AISC specification requirements is selected from some 98 rolled WF shapes. The program handles axial loads and moments due to gravity, dead and live loads, temperature, and wind.

Input

Job Number
Maximum Depth of Shape, in inches
Column Mark
Gravity Axial Load, in kips
Temperature Axial Load, in kips
Axial Load Due to Wind on X Axis, in kips
Axial Load Due to Wind on Y Axis, in kips
Gravity Moment about X Axis, in foot-kips
Gravity Moment about Y Axis, in foot-kips
Temperature Moment about X Axis, in foot-kips
Temperature Moment about Y Axis, in foot-kips
Wind Moment about X Axis, in foot-kips
Wind Moment about Y Axis, in foot-kips
Unbraced Length of Column, in inches.
Effective Length Factor
Yield Strength of Steel, kips per square inch
Coefficient Used in Formula 7a, Section 1.6 of AISC Specification

Output

Echo Print of Input Data
EFF = efficiency for loads due to gravity and temperature, where efficiency
  = $f_a/F_a + f_{bx}/F_{bx} + f_{by}/F_{by}$
EFFXW = efficiency for loads due to gravity, temperature, and wind on X Axis
EFFYW = efficiency for loads due to gravity, temperature, and wind on Y Axis
The Wide Flange Member Selected

Fig. 3.5   One-page abstract describing a steel column design program

Figure 3.6 shows a typical input sheet and Fig. 3.7 some typical output from such a program.

Although the second example program represents a considerably higher level of sophistication than the first by virtue of its use of table look-up procedures, code checking, and simultaneous handling of numerous loading conditions, it is in many respects similar to the first example in being representative of a special-purpose program that solves only part of the total structural design problem. Input to such a column-design program may well come from several other smaller programs: one for column axial loads, one for gravity moments in the column (such as those from the moment-distribution example), one for wind moments and shears, etc. Output from the column-design program might very well be used to

PROG. TITLE – COLUMN DESIGN
AISC – ROLLED AND COVER PLATED SECTION
PROG. NO. –
REQUESTED BY –
CHECKED BY –
DATE –
PAGE – OF –

HEADER CARD

ITEMS	AJNO	DLIM
UNITS		IN.
FORMAT	F8.2	F8.1
CARD COLS. 1 2 3 4 5 6 7 8 9 0	.5,6,1,1,1,1	2.5

DETAIL CARDS ONE FOR EACH COLUMN

ITEMS	CMK	PG	PT	PXW	PYW	BMXG	BMYG	BMXT	BMYT	BMXW	BMYW	H	K	FSY	CM
UNITS		KIPS	KIPS	KIPS	KIPS	FT.K.	FT.K.	FT.K.	FT.K.	FT.K.	FT.K.	IN.		K/IN²	
FORMAT	F8.2	F8.1	F5.0	F5.0	F5.0	F5.0	F5.0	F5.0	F5.0	F6.0	F6.0	F5.0	F4.1	F4.0	F4.2
	1,0,5	6,5,2		1,3	1,0	4,0	1,3			8,6	5,2	1,3,4	17	3,6	8,5
	1,0,2	8,7,8		2,9	2,2	4,0	1,3			19,0	1,1,7	2,0,4	17	3,6	8,5
CARD COLS.															

INSTRUCTIONS: LOCATION OF DECIMAL POINT IS INDICATED BY DOTTED LINE, ENTER DATA ACCORDINGLY

Fig. 3.6   Input sheet for steel-column design

STEEL COL. DESIGN—ROLLED + COVER PLATED SECTS.—OMITTING NEW HEAVY SECTIONS

CMK	PG	PT	PXW	PYW	BMXG	BMYG	BMXT	BMYT
1.05	652.0	0.	13.	10.	40.	13.	0.	0.
5611.11	25.0	EFF	0.952		EFFXW 0.847			EFFYW 0.945
1.02	878.0	0.	29.	22.	40.	13.	0.	0.
5611.11	25.0	EFF	0.793		EFFXW 0.757			EFFYW 0.928

Fig. 3.7 Output from steel-column design program

design lower-story girders for limiting wind drift, or for estimating purposes, or for designing baseplates, footings, etc. In short, though special-purpose programs have been and will continue to be quite useful, their fragmented nature is becoming increasingly apparent against the background of current developments in systems like STRUDL.

3.3 Mechanical Engineering*

The use of computers in mechanical applications to buildings has, to date, been relatively limited. In the mechanical disciplines of heating, piping, and air conditioning, one of the major successful applications has been in computations of heat gain and heat loss. Numerous programs exist today to perform these calculations. The simpler programs can run on very small computers and require only modest input and computation. The more complex programs may require several man-days of input preparation in order to run a more comprehensive analysis of the complete building.

These more complex heat-gain–heat-loss programs led the way to energy studies and to modeling the performance of a building throughout the course of a year. To date, however, such complete energy-study programs are restricted to larger machines and are relatively costly to run. Aside from the heat-gain–heat-loss and energy programs, initial progress is also being made in applying computer techniques to the problems of duct systems, fan selection, cooling coils, etc.[5]

A program for analyzing and designing cooling coils has been selected as an example of the kind of program that may be increasingly used in mechanical offices. Like the structural applications discussed above, this example is typical of current office applications in being a moderate-sized program that is addressed to the isolated problem of the analysis of a single component of the total mechanical system. Perhaps even more important, however, this example program indicates that it is possible to go beyond the easier task of analysis and to give the engineer the facility

* This application is based in part on Reference 4. Used by permission.

BMXW	BMYW	H	K	FSY	CM
86.	52.	134.	1.7	36.0.85	
				14WF	158
190.	117.	204.	1.7	36.0.85	
				14WF	287

to interact with the computer in the basic engineering activity of component selection.

The cooling-coil program is thus a tool both for the analysis of a proposed or existing installation of a bank of coils and for the selection (design) of a bank of coils to meet existing environmental circumstances. Working with the analysis option and using the basic input data of cubic feet per minute, rows, and air and water temperatures, the program will compute the total and sensible heat and air and water velocities, select a K factor automatically, and compute the total gallons per minute and final water temperature required. In addition, if the coil is being designed rather than analyzed, the program will select the number of rows of the coils and the compatible number of coils, face area, tube face, length, and height. Any number of banks of coils can be grouped together into a system, and the total gallons per minute and the average return water temperature for the system will then be computed.

As an added measure of flexibility, the program halts after each coil has been analyzed or designed. If the results are satisfactory to the engineer, the coil is accepted as is. If, however, the results are for some reason unsatisfactory (wrong series, final water temperature too high, too many rows, water or air velocity too great, etc.), the engineer can correct these variables at the computer typewriter and have the coil computed on the basis of new data. The program can analyze or design coils in two fin spacings for coils made by most major American manufacturers.

Figure 3.8 shows a standard input form which the engineer uses to record the input data for the problem. Each of the terms shown in Fig. 3.8 is listed with explanatory comments.

Once the input from cards 1 and 2 has been read into the computer, the coil will be analyzed or designed and the quantities shown in Fig. 3.9 will be printed by the computer. Each of the terms shown in Fig. 3.9 is listed with explanatory comments.

Note that the original input is part of the final output. This provides a very valuable check on input and serves as a complete and permanent record of the entire calculation. Immediately after printing the output, the computer comes to a halt and the engineer is given an opportunity to

CARD 1

ITEMS	FJOB	SER	ROWS	FAS	TFS	TLS	HTS	QUAN	
UNITS	—	—	—	Sq ft	—	in	in	—	
FORMAT	F8.1	F8.1	F8.1	F8.1	F8.1	F8.1	F8.1	F8.1	
CARD COLS									
	59.16	0	8	1.79	24	78	37	3	
	59.53	0	8	16.9	2.1	84	33	6	
	59.16	0	8	1.93	24	84	37	6	
	59.16	0	8	2.21	24	96	37	6	
	59.16	0	8	23.0	21	114	33	8	
	59.53	0	8	20.7	24	90	37	10	

CARD 2

ITEMS	DBI	WBI	ENTHI	WATI	DBF	WBF	ENTHF	WATF	CFM	
UNITS	F	F	Btu per lb	F	F	F	Btu per lb	F	Cu ft per min	
FORMAT	F8.1	F8.1	F8.1	F8.1	F8.1	F8.1	F8.1	F8.1	F8.1	
	83.7	66.5	31.2	43	51.5	50.2	20.4	53	271.00	
	83.6	68.3	32.7	42	49.0	48.4	19.4	52	470.00	
	83.7	66.5	31.2	43	51.5	50.2	20.4	53	545.00	
	83.7	66.5	31.2	43	51.5	50.2	20.4	53	652.00	
	82.6	66.0	30.8	43	53.5	52.3	21.6	53	922.00	
	82.3	67.5	32.0	42	52.0	51.0	20.9	54	1075.00	
CARD COLS										

Instructions: 1 Location of decimal point is indicated by dotted line; enter data accordingly.
2 Two cards for each bank of coils is required.

Fig. 3.8   Input sheet for cooling-coil analysis/design

Card 1

FJOB	job number
SER	series (fin spacing). Use 0 if lower fin spacing is required. Use 9 if higher fin spacing is required
ROWS	number of rows in coil
FAS	face area of one coil, square feet
TFS	tube face for one coil
TLS	tube length of one coil, inches
HTS	tube height of one coil, inches
QUAN	number of coils in bank

Card 2

DBI	dry bulb initial, °F
WBI	wet bulb initial, °F
ENTHI	enthalpy initial, Btu per pound
WATI	water initial, °F
DBF	dry bulb final, °F
WBF	wet bulb final, °F
ENTHF	enthalpy final, Btu per pound
WATF	final water temperature (estimated), °F
CFM	cubic feet per minute of air

Note: At the end of each system of banks, there must be a blank card.

check the results, modify the original input, change the physical size of a selected coil, etc. This kind of flexibility at the console of the computer is one of the advantages of a small-scale, moderately priced office computer, and provides the engineer with a vital link in the overall man-machine communications system.

```
AEROFIN COOLING COIL
     FJOB      SERIES      ROWS
   5916.00        .00      8.00
      FAS        TFS        TLS        HTS       QUAN
    17.90      24.00      78.00      37.00       3.00
      DBI        WBI      ENTHI       WATI
    83.70      66.50      31.20      43.00
      DBF        WBF      ENTHF       WATF        CFM
    51.50      50.20      20.40      53.00    27100.00

     QUAN        FAS        TFA        TFS        HTS        TLS
     3.00      17.90      53.70      24.00      37.00      78.00
   SERIES        ROW         TH         SH        SHF       TCFM
      .00       7.91  1302426.00   942429.60       .72    27100.00
      FPM        FPS        GPM       TGPM       WATI       WATF
   504.65       2.41      46.93     140.80      43.00      61.50
```

Fig. 3.9   Output from a typical coil analysis

The above output consists of a listing of original input plus:

QUAN	final number of coils in bank
FAS	face area selected for one coil, square feet
TFA	total face area (QUAN × FAS), square feet
TFS	tube face for one coil
HTS	height of one coil, inches
TLS	length of one coil, inches
SER	coil (fin spacing), where 0 indicates lower fin series, 9 indicates higher fin series
ROW	computed number of rows
TH	total heat, Btu
SH	sensible heat, Btu
SHF	sensible heat factor = SH/TH
TCFM	total cubic feet per minute for bank
FPM	feet per minute (air velocity)
FPS	feet per second (water velocity)
GPM	gallons per minute for one coil.
TGPM	total gallons per minute for bank
WATI	initial water temperature, °F
WATF	final water temperature, °F

3.4   Electrical Engineering

The use of computer techniques in building-industry electrical applications has been even more limited than in mechanical engineering, though interest does seem to be developing in the area. One example application that has met with moderate success is the problem of room-illumination computations.

Several firms, as well as lighting manufacturers, have prototype programs available for performing the computations involved in illumination studies. The basic input to the programs is essentially the geometric data and reflection coefficients of the room, plus information on the luminaire under investigation and a statement of either the required footcandle level or the number of luminaires to be installed. If the footcandle level is given, the number of luminaires required to produce that illumination level is computed. Conversely, if the number of luminaires is given, the actual level of illumination produced is computed.

Because the number of types of available illumination units is so large, it is convenient to select the most commonly used types, catalog them into a library, and store the pertinent information for each type (such as maintenance factor, data on coefficient of utilization, number of lamps, or size) in computer bulk storage. Then the engineer can simply select the type of luminaire he wishes to try from the library, and the appropriate technical data on that type are immediately available for internal computation. Some illumination programs even go a step further and include the initial cost and the operating costs in the computations, so that an economic comparison between different installations can be made.

3.5   Architectural Engineering

In a certain sense, nearly any computer application that contributes to the overall design of a building could be classified as an architectural or architectural-engineering application. By tradition, however, certain disciplines such as structural, mechanical, and electrical have been marked off and assigned their own sphere of specialized activity. Even with these disciplines taking their share of the applications, a large area of potential applications remains which might be called either architectural or architectural-engineering applications (the division between these two disciplines being somewhat arbitrary). Two examples from this rather large area of potential applications are discussed here. Other examples are discussed in Chapter 8.

A novel, yet useful, application of computer techniques to the problems of design of high-rise office and apartment buildings is that of elevatoring. Typically, the determination of the size and shape of the interior core of a building has a critical influence at the preliminary design stage on the layout and general character of the total building. In addition, the cost of an elevator system is a significant portion of the cost of a high-rise project. For both these reasons, it is important to have a reliable means of determining the number and size of elevator cabs required. The modest computer program described below has provided that capability for a number of high-rise projects.

The basic input for elevatoring a building might be thought of as consisting of four parts, as listed below:

1. Building data
   Number of floors
   Story heights for first, second, and typical floors
   Building population
2. Zone data
   Number of local floors served in the zone
   Number of express floors below this zone
   Zone population
   Number and depth of basements to be served
   Percent of up time used in down traffic (for two-way peak traffic)
3. Cab data
   Size (usually given in pounds of capacity, such as 3,500 pounds)
   Speed
   Door width
   Type of door
4. Elevatoring criteria
   Waiting time
   Emptying capacity

   Note: One of these two elevatoring criteria normally controls the number, size, and speed of cab used.

At this point, it should be pointed out that this example elevator program operates within the PLAN environment,* in order to give maximum flexibility and to encourage interaction between the designer and the machine. To that end, PLAN capabilities have been used to construct a simple problem-oriented language which makes communication with the computer remarkably easy.

The only command which the user need remember is "elevator program." Upon typing this command at the keyboard, he is furnished with the list of available commands and some explanatory notes on use of the system, as shown in Fig. 3.10.

The user may then type any or all of the available commands, with any or all of the listed data, in any order he chooses, and in free format. Even some misspelling is allowed, as long as the first three letters of each word are correct. Figure 3.11 indicates how typical commands look when typed

---

* PLAN, for Problem Language Analyzer, was developed by Jack Sams and his colleagues in the Manufacturing Industry Applications Group at IBM. For a fuller description of this interesting and eminently useful piece of work, the advanced reader is referred to IBM 1130 Data Presentation System, *Programmer's Manual,* Appendix C.

elevator program
listed below are the commands available for elevator program.
they may be used in any order.
only tne data items listed with **** must be given by the user.
the remaining data items are assumed to have the value shown,
   if not explicitly given by the user.

building data
nflrs****
first   20 ft
second   12.5 ft
typical   12.5
bpop****

zone data
local****
express   0
zpop   0
nbas   0
dbas   0
pcd   0

cab data
size   3500 lb
speed   500 feet/minute
dwidth   48 inches
key   2 (center opening, use 1 for side opening)

waiting time
wtime   30 seconds

emptying capacity
ec   13 percent in 5 minutes

select elevators

Fig. 3.10   Computer response to the command "elevator program"

by the user at the console. Once the building data, zone data, and cab data commands have been given, the command "select elevators" makes a few validity checks on the data and links to a program which calculates the total round-trip time for the elevator size and speed selected, taking into account loading and unloading times, number of probable stops, door time, acceleration/deceleration time, express and local time, lost time, etc. The program then determines the number of elevators of the given size to meet the waiting-time and emptying-capacity requirements.

building data, nflrs 20 first 16 second 20 bpop 1600;
cab data, size 3500 speed 500 dwidth 42;
zone data, local 10 zpop 840;

Fig. 3.11   Typical use of elevator commands

Figure 3.12 shows the results of the "select elevator" command for the final run of the elevator program on a recent twenty-story building in New York. Note that three different sets of answers for the low-rise zone shown select elevators;

nflrs	first	second	typical	bpop	pc	in min	mwt
20.	16.	20.	12.5	1600.	13.	5.	30.
size	speed	dwid	key	(dt)			
3500.	500.	42.	2.	0.0			
local	express	zpop	nbas	dbas	pcd		
10.	0.	840.	0.	0.	0.		

no. of cars=	4	5	6
wt tm (sec)=	36.0	28.8	24.0
pc in 5. m=	18.8	23.6	28.3

Fig. 3.12   Results of the command "select elevators"

here are computed. In particular, the program shows what the waiting time and emptying capacity (percent of population that can be accommodated in five minutes) are in the event that one fewer or one more cab than the mathematical optimum is selected. This is a very important feature, for it gives an indication of what the elevatoring will be like if the optimum number of cabs cannot be accommodated in the design.

General use of this program has indicated that the designer can rapidly gain a feeling for the critical elevator parameters of his building at the computer console. Typically, a number of different combinations of elevator sizes and speeds and zoning arrangements are tried before a satisfactory solution is obtained. The computer thus provides an ability to simulate the elevator-traffic problem and arrive at a reasonably optimum solution in a very short time.

A second example application in architectural engineering has been selected not so much for its practical utility in a single office but because it is representative of a larger class of architectural and engineering problems that is primarily logical in nature, rather than computational. An example of such a problem is the building-code problem described below.

As a prototype, portions of the Chicago Building Code have been placed on the computer. In the early stages of the design of a project, it is generally necessary to make a code analysis on the basis of certain minimal information regarding the proposed number of stories, height, floor area, frontage, location, etc. By providing this basic information, the designer can initiate at the computer typewriter a conversation such as that represented in Fig. 3.13. (The statements prefaced with a C indicate responses from the computer.) Once certain key questions regarding type of building, automatic sprinkling, etc., have been answered, a code analysis is printed out on the line printer (Fig. 3.14). On the basis of the given information concerning type and size of building, the computer has essentially made all the logical decisions implied by the fine print in the code, and

```
C   PLACE DATA CARD WITH BUILDING NAME, OCCUPANCY CLASS, ETC.
C   IN CARD READER AND PUSH START
C   IS THIS A PLAN DEVELOPMENT BUILDING
    NO
C   IS THIS BUILDING EQUIPPED WITH AUTOMATIC SPRINKLERS
    NO
C      TABLE 5 UPDATED
C   MAXIMUM STORY             1–A          9999
C   MAXIMUM HEIGHT            1–A          9999
C   MAXIMUM FLOOR AREA        1–B          9999
C   REQUIRED CONSTRUCTION TYPE  1–A
C   IS THIS TYPE ACCEPTABLE
    YES
```

Fig. 3.13   Man-machine conversation for a code analysis

has determined the type of construction required, listed the maximum height, floor area, and number of stories permitted for that type of construction (9999 means no limit), and proceeded to catalog the required fire rating for various elements of the building, complete with some explanatory notes. Numerous extensions to such a program to include exit requirements, stair widths, fire towers, structural loadings, etc., can easily be conceived.

From a practical point of view, it probably is not worthwhile for a single office to computerize large sections of numerous building codes. What may be economically justified, however, is for city building and zoning commissions to do so for their own code, and then make this service available—either free or for fee—to the practicing professional.

3.6   STRUDL—A Structural Design Language

This last portion of this chapter discusses briefly a language and large-scale computer system for solving structural analysis and design problems. Such a presentation is offered for two main reasons: first, because of the inherent capability which it offers to the practicing structural engineer and, second, because it seems very likely that developments in other engineering disciplines will eventually follow the pioneering work represented by the STRUDL effort.

To furnish some perspective on STRUDL, it should be pointed out that it evolved from the original STRESS program and is being developed under the Integrated Civil Engineering Systems (ICES) at M.I.T.[6,7,8] The first phase of ICES development incorporates seven subsystems as shown in Fig. 3.15.

The PROJECT subsystem forms the basis of the work presented in Chapter 7. A subsystem for architectural space, surface, and activity allocations, BUILD, is a part of phase II ICES development and is described in Chap-

CODE ANALYSIS
EQUITABLE BUILDING

APPLICABLE CODES
ZONING   CHICAGO ZONING ORDINANCE
                MUNICIPAL CODE OF CHICAGO
BUILDING   CHICAGO BUILDING CODE

OCCUPANCY CLASSIFICATION
CLASS E. BUSINESS

NO. FLOORS	AREA		NO. STORIES	HEIGHT
10.	19070.		1.	27.50
4.	18570.		32.	12.33
7.	18291.		2.	16.75
12.	17363.			
1.	12537.			
1.	62492.			
	675785. TOTAL AREA			455.66 TOTAL HEIGHT

NO AUTOMATIC SPRINKLERS
FRONTAGE   300. FT
PERIMETER   700. FT.

TYPE OF CONSTRUCTION REQUIRED, HEIGHT AND AREA LIMITATIONS
TYPE   1–A
STORIES   NO LIMITATIONS
HEIGHT   NO LIMITATIONS
AREA   NO LIMITATIONS

REQUIRED FIRE RESISTANCE IN HOURS

EXTERIOR BEARING WALLS	4D
EXTERIOR NONBEARING WALL OUTSIDE EXP.	2D
EXTERIOR NONBEARING WALL INSIDE EXP.	3
INTERIOR BEARING WALLS	4
EXTERIOR COLUMNS	4
INTERIOR COLUMNS SUPPORTING ROOF ONLY	3
OTHER INTERIOR COLUMNS	4
BEAMS, GIRDERS, TRUSSES, ROOF ONLY	2K
OTHER BEAMS, GIRDERS, TRUSSES	3
FLOOR CONSTRUCTION	3

NOTE D SUBTRACT ONE HOUR IF WALL FACES 30 FT OPEN SPACE.
NOTE K SEE 49–8 (K) FOR NOTE.

Fig. 3.14   Output from a prototype code analysis

ter 9. The STRUDL subsystem will be discussed in the remaining portion of this chapter.

Perhaps the most effective way to demonstrate the essential nature of the external characteristics of STRUDL is by means of an example problem. It should be pointed out, however, that this is not an attempt to provide comprehensive information on how to use the system. Instead, the emphasis is on the general nature of the language and the capabilities which the system provides.

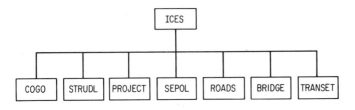

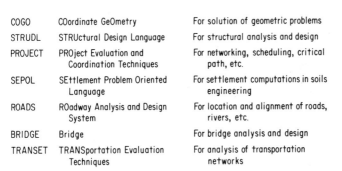

COGO	COordinate GeOmetry	For solution of geometric problems
STRUDL	STRUctural Design Language	For structural analysis and design
PROJECT	PROject Evaluation and Coordination Techniques	For networking, scheduling, critical path, etc.
SEPOL	SEttlement Problem Oriented Language	For settlement computations in soils engineering
ROADS	ROadway Analysis and Design System	For location and alignment of roads, rivers, etc.
BRIDGE	Bridge	For bridge analysis and design
TRANSET	TRANSportation Evaluation Techniques	For analysis of transportation networks

Fig. 3.15   Phase I subsystems of ICES

Figure 3.16 illustrates a typical three-bay three-story plane frame. As in all structural analysis and design problems, one of the first steps is to describe the geometry and loading on the structure. Figure 3.17 illustrates the description of the problem to the computer in the STRUDL language commands.

The PROBLEM* command gives the structure an identifying name, while

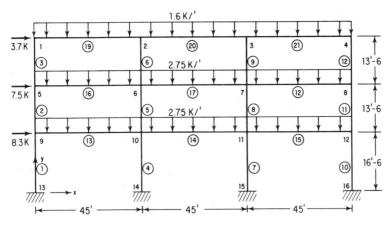

Fig. 3.16   Three-story plane frame for STRUDL example

* Uppercase phrases are actual STRUDL commands.

```
STRUDL
PROBLEM '5997' 'GRAND RAPIDS'
CONSTANTS E 4180000. ALL
TYPE PLANE FRAME XY
JOINT COORDINATES
1  X   0.  Y  0.
2  X  45.  Y  0.
...
MEMBER INCIDENCES
1  13  9
2   9  5
3   5  1
...
LOADING 'DL+LL'
MEMBER LOADS
13  FORCE Y UNIFORM  2.75
14  FORCE Y UNIFORM  2.75
...
LOADING 'WIND'
LOADING 'COMBINED' .75 'DL+LL'
                   .75 'WIND'
LOADING LIST 'DL+LL' 'COMBINED'
...
PRELIMINARY ANALYSIS
...
```

Fig. 3.17 STRUDL statements for description of the problem

the JOINT COORDINATES command lists the X and Y coordinates for each joint of the structure. The MEMBER INCIDENCES statement completes the geometrical description by giving the topological information on how the joints are connected by members (member 1 goes from joint 13 to joint 9, 2 from 9 to 5, etc.).

After the geometry has been specified, the designer lists the loads on the structure by means of the LOADING, MEMBER LOADS, and JOINT LOADS commands, as shown. Note also that it is possible to combine the effects of several loading combinations, by means of the COMBINED statement. The LOADING LIST command sets up a list of loading conditions (in this case loading 1 for gravity and loading 3 for combined gravity and wind) for which subsequent analysis and design will be performed.

Now that the geometry and loading information has been entered, the designer can either make some assumptions of member properties such as moments of inertia and cross-sectional areas, and execute an indeterminate STIFFNESS ANALYSIS, or he can issue the PRELIMINARY ANALYSIS command to make assumptions concerning the structural behavior, such as locations of points of zero moments or approximate shears in columns, and thereby execute a determinate analysis without making use of member properties. The latter case is shown in the example where a PRELIMINARY ANALYSIS command has been used.

Results of the PRELIMINARY ANALYSIS command are a set of axial thrusts, shears, and moments at each end of each member. Having these preliminary member forces available, it is now possible to consider the problem of member selection (design) to meet a specified code.

```
ADD PARAMETERS
'CODE' USE 'AISC'
'FYLD' EQ 36.
'NOMD' EQ 14  FOR MEMBERS 1 TO 12
        EQ 30  FOR MEMBERS 13 TO 18
        LE 27  FOR MEMBERS 19 TO 21
'LY'    EQ 14  FOR MEMBERS 1, 4, EQ 11 FOR 2, 5
  .
  .
  .

SELECT MEMBERS 1, 2, 4, 5 AS 'COLUMN' MEMBERS
SELECT MEMBERS 13, 14, 19 AS 'BEAM' MEMBERS
TAKE MEMBERS 13 TO 18 AS LARGEST OF MEMBERS 13, 14
  ON BASIS 'SZ'
TAKE MEMBERS 3, 11, 12  SAME AS MEMBER 2
  .
  .
  .

STIFFNESS ANALYSIS
LIST ALL
  .
  .
  .

CHECK MEMBERS 13 TO 21 FOR 'ZMOMENT'  'YSHEAR'
  .
  .
  .
```

Fig. 3.18   STRUDL statements for member selection and code checking

Figure 3.18 shows sample STRUDL commands to select members of the frame to satisfy the AISC code, using A36 steel with a yield point of 36 kips* per square inch. Certain architectural constraints are to be imposed on the nominal depth of the members, as indicated in the figure. In addition, some further information on the unbraced length LY for some of the columns is being provided by the designer. Critical column members 1, 2, 4, and 5 and beams 13, 14, and 19 are now selected by means of the SELECT MEMBER command. Results of the SELECT MEMBER command are shown in Fig. 3.19.

*For a more complete description of this part of STRUDL, see Reference 9, where the example in this discussion of STRUDL is also used.

MEMBER	PROFILE	CRITICAL LOADING	CRITICAL SECTION
1	14WF119	'DL+LL'	1.25
2	14WF78	'DL+LL'	1.25
...			
...			
19	27WF84	'DL+LL'	45.00

Fig. 3.19   Typical output from the SELECT MEMBER command

It is normal practice to select or design only a few typical or critical members in a structural design, with the remaining members being equated to these critical members. The TAKE MEMBERS command performs this member-equating task for the remaining members in the structure.

Now that all the members in the structure have been selected from appropriate tables of rolled sections, member properties are available and it is possible to execute an indeterminate STIFFNESS ANALYSIS. Results of a stiffness analysis include not only a set of axial thrusts, shears, and moments at each end of each member but also sets of support reactions and joint displacements, as shown in Fig. 3.20.

PROBLEM '5997' 'GRAND RAPIDS'
LOADING 'DL+LL'
MEMBER FORCES

MEMBER	JOINT	AXIAL FORCE	SHEAR FORCE	MOMENT
1	13	152.405	21.790	121.65
1	9	−152.405	−21.790	237.89
2	9	92.526	25.368	160.23
2	5	−92.526	−25.368	182.23
...				
...				

REACTIONS

JOINT	FORCE X	FORCE Y	MOMENT Z
13	21.790	−152.405	121.65
14	−0.805	−326.844	−4.21
15	0.805	−326.844	4.21
16	−21.790	−152.405	−121.65

JOINT DISPLACEMENTS

JOINT	X DISPLACEMENT	Y DISPLACEMENT	ROTATION
1	.00185	.00213	.00134
2	.00056	.00691	−.00014
...			
...			

Fig. 3.20   Selected output from the STIFFNESS ANALYSIS command

With a new set of member forces available, the designer can check the columns for combined axial load and moment and check the beams for moment and shear, as indicated by the CHECK MEMBERS command in Fig. 3.18.

At this point it should be obvious to the reader that a system such as

STRUDL goes considerably beyond typical current office applications as described earlier, in two important respects. First, the medium of communication is no longer a rigid input sheet composed of strings of digits, but instead is a flexible problem-oriented language developed especially for the structural engineer. This kind of problem-oriented language has been widely accepted, first in COGO and then in STRESS, by engineers across the nation. Such languages have probably done more than any other single capability to bring a wide range of engineering users into effective communication with modern computational techniques.

The second significant difference between a system like STRUDL and the current mode of office usage is the difference between handling the total analysis and design of all structural members as a systematic whole rather than as small isolated parts of the total structure. In the past, the labor associated with filling in input forms for column loads, another form for moment distribution, another for column design, etc., frequently meant such repetition that in some cases it was faster to perform a solution by hand than to use the computer. The unified treatment of all members of a structure with one flexible language eliminates this repetition of common input, and effectively combines the numerous smaller programs into a single information processor. It seems quite likely that this type of systematic treatment of the problem as a whole, in the environment of a problem-oriented language, may serve as a prototype for future developments, not only in structural engineering, but also in a variety of other engineering disciplines.

REFERENCES

1. Conference on Electronic Computation, *ASCE Structural Division Conference Papers*, Kansas City, 1958.
2. Second Conference on Electronic Computation, *ASCE Structural Division Conference Papers*, Pittsburgh, 1960.
3. Third Conference on Electronic Computation, *ASCE Structural Division Journal*, August, 1963.
4. G. Neil Harper, "Analysis and Design of Cooling Coils," *Heating, Piping and Air Conditioning*, Reinhold Publishing Corporation, New York, April, 1966.
5. *Proceedings of the HPAC Conference*, Reinhold Publishing Corporation, New York, 1966.
6. Daniel Roos, *ICES Systems Design*, The M.I.T. Press, Cambridge, Mass., 1966.
7. Fenves, Logcher, and Mauch, *STRESS, A User's Manual*, The M.I.T. Press, Cambridge, Mass., 1965.
8. R. D. Logcher, et al., *ICES STRUDL 1—Engineering User's Manual*, M.I.T. Department of Civil Engineering, Cambridge, Mass., 1968.
9. G. N. Harper and R. D. Logcher, "Member Selection Commands for Structural Design," *Journal of the Structural Division, American Society of Civil Engineers*, February, 1968.

CHAPTER FOUR   *Specifications*

By G. Neil Harper

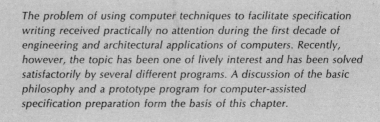

The problem of using computer techniques to facilitate specification writing received practically no attention during the first decade of engineering and architectural applications of computers. Recently, however, the topic has been one of lively interest and has been solved satisfactorily by several different programs. A discussion of the basic philosophy and a prototype program for computer-assisted specification preparation form the basis of this chapter.

4.1 Statement of the Specification-writing Problem*

The preparation of a set of specifications to accompany design drawings is an essential activity for every professional office. Working drawings and specifications, historically speaking, are the visible product of the design office; they are also the instruments that communicate the designer's concept both to the client and to the contractor. Hence a concise and accurate set of specifications is a vital link in the complete building sequence from conception to execution.

The volume of specification work within a particular office will vary greatly with office philosophy, size of office, and size of project. Specifications may vary from only one or two pages for smaller sections to fifty or more pages for a complicated set of mechanical or structural specifications. With several jobs in the office at one time and with several sections of specifications on each job, it is obvious that time spent in specification writing and editing can become a significant part of the expense of the job.

This situation has led to a variety of attempts to reduce the cost of preparing specifications. One method has been to have preprinted specifications covering the general job conditions. Such a procedure has much in its favor insofar as a large part of any job can be accommodated by a single general specification. However, every job will also vary to a greater or lesser degree from the requirements of this general preprinted specification. To cover the specific job requirements, it has therefore been necessary to append a handwritten set of "special conditions" to the preprinted specification covering general conditions.

In contrast to the preprinted specification, many offices essentially write the specification for each job completely by hand—frequently using a past job specification as a guide. Aside from the cost and time required by this procedure, it seems to be a poor investment of a professional's time to write documents which are largely repetitive.

The unsuitability of either the preprinted specification or the completely handwritten specification has led to a new approach in specification writing that uses the best features of both methods. This third approach takes advantage of the repetitive nature of the specification where such exists, yet allows the architect or engineer to select or add at his discretion to customize the specification for the job at hand.

The basic concept involved in this approach is that a library of more or less standard specification sections is used, as needed, and is modified and supplemented by special paragraphs to produce the final job specification.

* This chapter is based in part on Reference 1. Used by permission.

This has been the essential concept in all automated specification systems developed to date.

This basic concept has been implemented both on automatic typewriters and on high-speed computers.* The automatic-typewriter systems typically are driven by one or more paper-tape readers, magnetic tapes, edge-card readers, etc. Such systems run essentially at automatic-typewriter speed, and require constant attention by an operator to skip paragraphs, add paragraphs manually, and update subparagraph numbers, page numbers, etc. Although this system, relative to a computer-driven system, is somewhat crude and slow, it has produced satisfactory specifications for several consulting offices.[3]

The combination of high-speed computer capability with the concept of selective specification writing is beginning to produce remarkable results, and is the principal subject matter of this chapter. This approach permits additions, deletions, and modifications to be done off-line (away from the computer) at a standard keypunch. Then the entire job specification can be produced in a matter of a few minutes on a computer-driven high-speed printer, and without operator intervention. The job specification can be printed directly on good-quality paper, photo-offset master, stencils, or ditto masters, from which multiple copies may be made by standard reproducing techniques.

4.2 A Prototype Computer Program for Specifications

Any computerized specification program is essentially a combination of two elements—a computer program and a library of architectural and engineering specifications which have been punched into cards and/or loaded on a disk or magnetic tape. The computer program provides the guiding logic that controls the flow of the specifications library from punched cards, disk, or tape to the final computer-printed job specification. The specifications library is a comprehensive master specification. Any block of information in the library (such as a line, paragraph, or section) can be omitted from the final job specification simply by listing the numbers of the lines to be omitted on a punched card.

Figure 4.1 shows diagrammatically the sequence of producing a job specification using the system. Each line of information in the master specification has a unique identification number listed in the left margin alongside the line of information. To omit any line of information, this

* A good summary of current (1967) usage can be found in Reference 2.

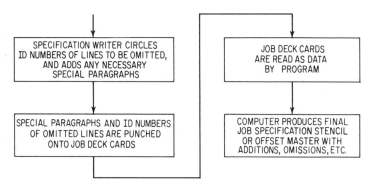

Fig. 4.1   Operational sequence for producing a job specification

number is simply checked or circled by the specification writer. The numbers which have been circled are punched into cards by a keypunch operator and then used as input data for the program which prints the final job specification.

Ideally, the master specification should be written to include as many specification alternates as possible. Nevertheless, there will always be some sections where hand finishing and rewriting are necessary. This rewriting and addition of material can be inserted by hand exactly as in the past when the specification writer was working with an old job specification or a standard specification as a guide. This additional material is then punched into cards and included as a part of the data to be used for that particular job.

Two points concerning handwritten additions and corrections deserve emphasis, however. The first is that there is absolutely no change in the current procedure of making additions and corrections as far as the specifications writer is concerned. The second point is that this type of addition should be avoided as far as possible by constructing a comprehensive master specification. Alternates for various manufacturers, differing geographical locations, contractor practices, etc., can all be handled by a well-worded standard specification with suitable alternate paragraphs.

4.3   Example Problem

To demonstrate how alternate paragraphs, omissions, additions, and modifications are used in editing a master specification to produce a job specification, part of a typical section on structural steel has been selected for illustration. Figure 4.2 presents the master or guide specification as it might appear after editing by the specification writer.

Several items are worthy of note here. First, the identification number of

```
080010A                    SECTION 8  STRUCTURAL STEEL


080020B     08-01.   GENERAL AND SPECIAL CONDITIONS


080030C           A.  THE SECTIONS 'GENERAL CONDITIONS' AND 'SPECIAL
080040      CONDITIONS' FORM A PART OF THIS SECTION.


080050B     08-02.   WORK SPECIFIED ELSEWHERE


080060C           A.  SETTING ANCHOR BOLTS AND BASE PLATES ------ SECTION 6
                  B.  Ornamental Iron Work ――――――― Section 53
                  C.  Survey and Bench Marks ――――――― Section 17


080070B     08-03.   GENERAL


080080C           A.  THE CONTRACTOR SHALL ENGAGE, AT HIS OWN EXPENSE,
080090C           A.  THE OWNER SHALL ENGAGE, AT HIS OWN EXPENSE,
080100      A TESTING LABORATORY APPROVED BY THE ARCHITECT TO INSPECT HIGH
080110      STRENGTH BOLTED CONNECTIONS AND WELDS AND TO PERFORM ALL TESTS
080120      AND SUBMIT TEST REPORTS TO THE ARCHITECT.
                    including erection sequences, schedules, and completed details
080130C           B.  SHOP DRAWINGS---SHOP DRAWINGS SHALL BE SUBMITTED
080140      TO THE ARCHITECT FOR APPROVAL.

080150C           C.  ANCHOR BOLTS---FURNISH ANCHOR BOLTS AND SETTING PLANS
080160      IN AMPLE TIME TO PREVENT DELAY TO OTHER TRADES.  ANCHOR BOLTS
080170      SHALL BE SET WITH TEMPLATES AS SPECIFIED IN THE SECTION CONCRETE.

080180C           D.  FITTING OF STRUCTURAL MEMBERS---THE CONTRACTOR ALONE
080190      SHALL BE RESPONSIBLE FOR THE CORRECT FITTING OF ALL STRUCTURAL
080200      MEMBERS AND FOR THE ELEVATION AND ALIGNMENT OF THE FINISHED
080210      STRUCTURE.

080220C           E.  ADJUSTMENTS---ANY ADJUSTMENTS NECESSARY IN THE STEEL
080230      FRAME BECAUSE OF DISCREPANCIES IN ELEVATIONS AND ALIGNMENT SHALL
080240      BE THE RESPONSIBILITY OF THE CONTRACTOR.

080250Z           NOTE TO SPEC WRITER---MILL REPORTS ARE REQUIRED
080260Z           ONLY ON JOBS IN STATES OF ILLINOIS AND MICHIGAN.

080270            F.  MILL REPORTS---FURNISH TO THE ARCHITECT TWO CERTIFIED
080280      COPIES OF MILL REPORTS COVERING THE CHEMICAL AND PHYSICAL PROPER-
080290      TIES OF ALL STEEL USED IN THIS WORK.

            MASTER SPEC            8 - 01                      5/31/61
              Grand Rapids                                     595701
```

Fig. 4.2 An edited master specification

each line is found in the left margin. A circle around any of these numbers
will omit the corresponding line in the job specification. At lines 080080C
and 080090C, note the manner in which a paragraph which normally varies
by only one word is handled. Note, too, that information has been added
after block 080060C. Line 080130C has information added in the center of
the line. Such a procedure normally should be avoided by suitable word-
ing. When necessary this type of addition can be handled, as it would be
here, by retyping the lines affected and treating the correction as a simple
addition (omitting the original lines 080130C and 080140). Note that the
omission of lines 080150C, 080160, and 080170 implies that the following

paragraph headings should be changed from D to C, E to D, etc. This, plus several other levels of subparagraph updating, is executed automatically. As shown in Fig. 4.2, it is also possible to include instructions to the specification writer in the body of the standard specification. These intraoffice instructions can be automatically omitted when the job specification is actually printed by the computer. Such a facility can prove valuable in maintaining a consistently high-quality specification in an office where several people are charged with the responsibility of specification writing.

The example illustrated by Fig. 4.2 encompasses the most frequent kind of editing work performed on specifications—additions, deletions, alternates, and updating. With only the handwritten information from Fig. 4.2 and the ID numbers of omitted lines punched as data, the computer program combines the master specification from cards, tape, or disk with the new information implied by the editing to produce the job specification shown in Fig. 4.3. Note the lack of ID numbers in the margin, inclusion of material which has been added by hand, updating of paragraph labels, and the job line at the bottom of the page.

The general program logic followed in producing a set of job specifications from the master library is outlined in Fig. 4.4. The extreme simplicity in the general concept is a direct result of viewing the specification-writing process essentially as one of omission, addition, or both, to a body of textual material that is largely repetitive in nature from job to job.

The implications from even a casual observation of Figs. 4.2 and 4.3 should be obvious. Proper use of computer assistance in specification preparation can lead to significant reductions in preparation costs. In addition, the burden of proofreading has been reduced to the minor task of reading the new information added by hand and checking the adequacy of omissions. No longer need the specification writer worry about misspelled words or incorrect punctuation. The clerical time saved can be spent in research on new materials and construction techniques, development of more lucid master specifications, and better engineering design. The most striking advantage, however, is the rapidity with which the job specification can now be produced. Because reproducible masters for the complete job can be produced automatically in a matter of minutes, this final operation can be delayed until the design is virtually complete, thus eliminating errors and changes associated with simultaneous preparation of drawings and specifications.

4.4   New Developments

A modified version of the prototype program described above was originally coded and demonstrated on a medium-sized computer. The

```
                    SECTION 8  STRUCTURAL STEEL


08-01.   GENERAL AND SPECIAL CONDITIONS


       A. THE SECTIONS 'GENERAL CONDITIONS' AND 'SPECIAL
CONDITIONS' FORM A PART OF THIS SECTION.


08-02.   WORK SPECIFIED ELSEWHERE


       A. SETTING ANCHOR BOLTS AND BASE PLATES --------- SECTION  6

       B. ORNAMENTAL IRON WORK --------------------- SECTION 53

       C. SURVEYS AND BENCH MARKS ------------------- SECTION 17


08-03.   GENERAL


       A. THE CONTRACTOR SHALL ENGAGE, AT HIS OWN EXPENSE,
A TESTING LABORATORY APPROVED BY THE ARCHITECT TO INSPECT HIGH
STRENGTH BOLTED CONNECTIONS AND WELDS AND TO PERFORM ALL TESTS
AND SUBMIT TEST REPORTS TO THE ARCHITECT.

       B. SHOP DRAWINGS---SHOP DRAWINGS INCLUDING ERECTION
SEQUENCES, SCHEDULES, AND COMPLETED DETAILS SHALL BE SUBMITTED
TO THE ARCHITECT FOR APPROVAL.

       C. FITTING OF STRUCTURAL MEMBERS---THE CONTRACTOR ALONE
SHALL BE RESPONSIBLE FOR THE CORRECT FITTING OF ALL STRUCTURAL
MEMBERS AND FOR THE ELEVATION AND ALIGNMENT OF THE FINISHED
STRUCTURE.

       D. ADJUSTMENTS---ANY ADJUSTMENTS NECESSARY IN THE STEEL
FRAME BECAUSE OF DISCREPANCIES IN ELEVATIONS AND ALIGNMENT SHALL
BE THE RESPONSIBILITY OF THE CONTRACTOR.

       E. MILL REPORTS---FURNISH TO THE ARCHITECT TWO CERTIFIED
COPIES OF MILL REPORTS COVERING THE CHEMICAL AND PHYSICAL PROPER-
TIES OF ALL STEEL USED IN THIS WORK.

       F. TEMPLATES---FURNISH TEMPLATES, WHERE SHOWN OR CALLED
FOR ON THE DRAWINGS.  FURNISH SHIM PLATES OR DEVELOPED FILLS
WHERE REQUIRED TO OBTAIN PROPER FIT AND ALIGNMENT.


GRAND RAPIDS            8 - 01                  5957.01
```

Fig. 4.3 The resulting job specification

program was never actually used for production, however, primarily because at the time it was coded (1964), there was no standard computer equipment on the market to print upper- and lowercase characters. Since that time, however, computer hardware for upper- and lowercase characters has been developed, and at least two major general-purpose text-editing computer programs are available to produce textual output.*

Figure 4.5 is a sample of the computer output of a master specification

* Perhaps the first such upper- and lowercase program, the so-called "Text 90" program, runs on the large-scale IBM 7090 computer and has been used to produce the programming manuals for the IBM 360 system. A second and similar program, "Datatext," is available commercially in several major United States cities.

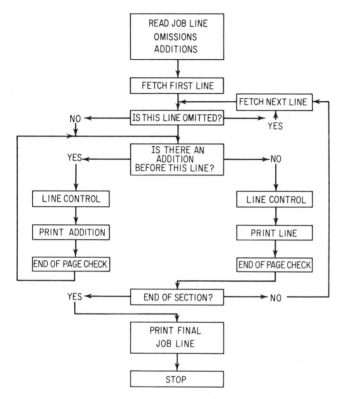

Fig. 4.4   Program logic for specification preparation

which was written using the Text 90 program. The overall philosophy used in the prototype program described above is evident in the use of this program, which also works on a line-by-line basis as indicated by the line numbers in the left-hand margin. The alphabetic codes in the margin, such as NAX2, are edit codes for skipping lines, indenting, etc. Note that the lines are justified on the right margin as well as the left, and that all special characters such as underlining, colons, and quotes are available. This system also permits insertion of material in the middle of lines, replacing a word, such as "owner," with another word, such as "contractor," throughout the text, automatic checking of spelling, preparation of tables of contents, etc. Such a program produces specifications at a rate of about five to ten pages per minute.

4.5   Concluding Remarks

The philosophic premise underlying all the automated systems described above is that the specification writer must consciously omit material from the master specification to produce a job specification. There is, however,

SOM OFFICE STANDARD
CAISSONS

001001	NAX2	GENERAL NOTES AND INSTRUCTIONS TO SOM:
001002	S1I8J8	Strike out following paragraphs not applicable to this project.
001004	S2AX2	GENERAL CONDITIONS AND REQUIREMENTS:
001005	S1I4	The applicable sections of "General Conditions" and
001006		"General Requirements" form a part of this section.
001007	S2AX2	EXTENT OF WORK:
001008	S1I4	The extent of "caisson" work is shown on the drawings
001009		including location of caissons, diameters of shafts, diam-
001010		eters of bells where required for caissons on hardpan, esti-
001011		mated bottom elevations, top elevations, number, detail, and
001012		size of reinforcing steel if required, strength of concrete
001013		required and other pertinent details and notes.
001014	S2AX2	MATERIALS:
001015	S1	Portland Cement: ASTM C 150, Type I normal portland cement.
001016	S	Fly Ash: ASTM C 350.
001017	S	Plasticizing Admixtures: "Pozzolith" (Master Builders Co.);
001018		"Placewel-R" (Johns-Manville Co.) or "Plastiment" (Sika
001019		Chemical Corp.); type and quantity recommended by manu-
001020		facturer depending upon conditions at project site.
001021	S	Aggregate for Stone Concrete shall comply with ASTM C 33 and
001022		the following:
001023	S14J4	General: All aggregates when subject to 5 cycles of the
001024		sodium sulfate soundness test (ASTM C 88) shall not lose
001025		more than 15 percent by weight. Aggregates for the entire
001026		job shall come from the same source unless a change is
001027		approved by the architect.
001028	SIJ	Fine Aggregates: Natural or artificial hard, clean sand.
001029	SIJ	Coarse Aggregates: Gravel or crushed rock with clean, hard,
001030		uncoated particles, ASTM C 33, size 467.

Fig. 4.5 Sample output from the Text 90 text-editing program

another approach to specification writing that, in the long run, may prove even more fruitful. This approach is based on the concept of inclusion rather than omission. Under such a system, the specification writer might circle appropriate key words from a checklist or index, and these would be used directly to link a whole sequence of standard paragraphs from the master library to form a job specification. This intriguing idea, currently under study, has not yet been fully developed.

Another fascinating notion that is as yet only in the discussion phase is that eventually the building industry may have regional specification centers, with specifications on manufacturers' products available on a common basis from remote inquiry stations located in the professional offices. Discussion of this kind of possible future development is beyond scope of this chapter.

Computer programs such as the prototype program, Text 90, and Datatext have been used successfully in architectural and engineering offices to produce both master and job specifications. It should be pointed out, however, that automation of the clerical tasks of specification writing by no means solves the complete specification problem. Development and maintenance of the master specification can be a costly and time-consuming task, and education of personnel in the use of new systems is not always easy. In the final analysis, more lucid and efficient specifications require a considerable effort and will be produced only by a combination of top-level personnel and effective use of available automation techniques.

REFERENCES

1. G. Neil Harper, "Autospec: Automated Preparation of Specifications," *Journal of the Structural Division, American Society of Civil Engineers,* December, 1966.
2. "Around the Corner: Better Specifications," *A & E News,* December, 1966, pp. 38–45.
3. "Prepare Specifications in Half the Time," *Civil Engineering,* January, 1966, pp. 56–67.

CHAPTER FIVE *Computer-aided*
Cost-estimating Techniques

By Richard I. Krauss, AIA, and Theodore H. Myer

Although small segments of the cost-estimating problem have been solved with varying degrees of success, the solution of the total problem is one of considerable difficulty. A description of the problem —as seen from the architect's viewpoint—is followed by an outline of a very promising approach to its solution. The notion of complete "predictive estimating" forms the basis of the proposed approach. Interestingly enough, this rather simple-appearing problem may require some of the most advanced concepts in computer technology for its proper solution.

Mr. Krauss is an Associate in Ashley, Myer and Associates, and is serving simultaneously as Special Assistant to the Director, Institute for Applied Technology, National Bureau of Standards, Washington. He holds a B.A. degree from Harvard, 1957, and a B. Arch. from M.I.T., 1961. Mr. Krauss has been active since 1961 in architectural practice, and recently authored a study at M.I.T. on the design process, with Prof. John R. Myer, entitled "Design: A Case History."

Mr. Myer holds a B.A. degree from Harvard, 1959, and a B. Arch. from M.I.T., 1963. A consultant at Bolt, Beranek and Newman since 1963, he has been engaged in research in information sciences. His projects have included research on computer aids to architectural design, analysis of graphic data, and time-sharing systems. He is currently developing display equipment and associated graphic program systems.

5.1 Introduction*

The primary concerns of this chapter are to delineate the problems involved in performing cost estimates and to suggest approaches by which they might be solved if a general computer communication and calculation system were available. No attempt has been made to develop in detail ways of implementing such a computer system. Cost estimating in the building industry is a complex process involving numerous individuals with diverse interests; the material presented here has focused on the special needs of the architect and outlined an approach toward a computer-based estimating system to meet his needs.

The process of cost estimating entails three steps: first, stating what is to be priced; second, determining the prices in the marketplace; and third, multiplying and tabulating the costs.

For architects, the first step is most difficult because from the outset of a project until most of the architect's work is done there are neither a final design nor final contract documents adequate to establish a basis for accurate pricing. Hence, to establish something to price, the estimating system must be capable of *predicting* what is to be priced. This predictive capability is especially useful at the beginning of the design process when specific descriptions are difficult to make but a complete budget must be set up. As a project is developed, the architect wishes to keep track of budget changes as the design takes a particular form; hence the original complete, but predicted, "model" on which the early budgets are based should permit modification according to information which the architect now specifically *describes*.

Predictive estimating would be done by using a computer-stored body of general information about buildings, together with a program system for generating from this information a detailed "predicted" image of a specific building on the basis of statements from the designer concerning the type, size, and location of the project to be designed. This predicted image would be complete and would contain the same order of detail found in a final, prebid estimate. As design decisions were made, the architect would modify the stored image to reflect his evolving design by entering specific

* This chapter is based on a study, completed in 1965, sponsored by John P. Eberhard, Director of the Institute for Applied Technology, National Bureau of Standards. The study was conducted at M.I.T. under the direction of Profs. Albert G. H. Dietz and John R. Myer. A report of the study in more detail is available as "Computer-aided Cost Estimating Techniques for Architects," *Report* PB-174-098, Clearinghouse for Federal Scientific and Technical Information, Institute for Applied Technology, Washington, D.C.

information into the computer. This information would specify the materials and equipment comprising the building, the building geometry, and by means of various indexes, the degrees of construction quality or difficulty.

The next step in preparing for a cost estimate beyond defining what to price is that of gathering prices to apply. This step entails gathering information from the industry and storing it in such a way that it is retrievable at the appropriate time in the proper form. This implies a computer-stored library of in-place unit costs, derived by a subsidiary computer process from construction records of the kinds and amounts of labor, materials, and equipment required to produce each in-place building unit.

The final step in cost estimating is that of performing the calculations and producing the tabulations in appropriate form. In order to produce an estimate, a set of processes would, on demand, calculate and collect the quantity of each kind of material or equipment in the building, couple this information with unit costs extracted from the cost library, and produce tabulated cost summaries. By forming different groupings of the items comprising the building description, these processes would produce cost tabulations in a variety of formats suited to the architect or the contractor.

Sections 5.2 to 5.6 explore computer-based cost estimating from the viewpoint of the user of an estimating system. The needs of the designer are explored, and the idea of predictive estimating is developed as meeting certain of these needs. The kinds of specific cost-affecting information that are generated as the design progresses and means for entering them into the computer are discussed. Finally, the information comprising a cost library, and a means for calculating and tabulating estimated building costs are outlined.

Sections 5.7 to 5.11 explore the technical nature of the computer system. Its basic components are outlined and the structure of the data within the system is discussed. A basic vocabulary for entering specific design information is suggested. Approaches toward implementing the predictive estimating process and the cost-calculating process are presented.

Sections 5.12 and 5.13 discuss some of the technical and political implications of computer-based estimating, and summarize the chapter.

5.2 Needs of the Architect

The architect has a set of needs that place special demands on the form of a computer-based estimating system. These needs differ from those of the other trades in the construction industry.

The architect must make a complete estimate very early in the course of most design projects, even though at this point he has only fragmentary information about the desired design. Many times (especially with clients who have constituencies of investors or voters) the architect must furnish at the outset a budget that becomes binding. Additionally at first, the client can usually state only his need for a type of building (in terms of use), some form of the needed capacity, and some indication of location. Yet, in order to indicate to the client the cost implication of various design alternatives, the architect must infer some model of the building containing a great deal more specific information than the client supplies so that available cost figures can be meaningfully used. Hence, there is a need for an estimating system to provide a complete budget (hopefully with some indication of its variability), even though based on minimal and preliminary information from the client.

Designing, in a sense, can be looked upon as making explicit the needs and desires of the client and translating these into physical form; thus accurate communications with the client are a key part of the design process. Especially at the outset of the design procedure, the problem of accurately communicating about scope and intent is difficult and critical. The budget estimate forms an essential part of this communication process and sometimes forms the expression of the owner's chief concerns. Hence, for the architect, the budget must be able to serve as an accurate communication device.

As the project proceeds, there is always the need to keep track of the status of the budget and to keep track of how and why and when it is changing. This is a political and key problem to the architect in his relationship to the client and one on which much time and care is spent, usually by highly paid and responsible personnel. A record of budget changes can form a tool for keeping track of the decisions made in the design process and can readily improve the understanding of the financial status of a project. In order to fulfill this record-keeping function, the estimated budget must be able to reflect the cost consequences of any decisions as they are made, regardless of the stage of the design or the level of design statement—from very general statements down to statements about details and special materials. A computer-based estimating system, then, must permit estimates to be changed continuously, while allowing maintenance of accurate records of budget-affecting decisions. Hopefully, if done in a fashion accurate enough for contractors to accept, the budget-making system can then overcome the critical discontinuity that now exists when the budget responsibility shifts from the architect to the contractor (see Sec. 5.6).

An estimating tool meeting the above requirements could fulfill another need of the architect. A key factor in design decisions is often financial and yet, because of the enormity of the number of parts and interconnections of a building, the effect on cost of changes in materials or dimensions is difficult and expensive to take into account accurately. Thus one of the designer's needs is for a cost-estimating technique that will tell him the effect on the estimated cost of his project of alternate design decisions.

Another major problem an architect faces in establishing a budget is that of gathering information on which to base his calculations. There is, first, the problem of getting rough price information (e.g., "$20 per square foot") based only on the most general design information (e.g., "a school"). Second, there is the time-consuming and politically difficult problem of gathering accurate price information on quantities of materials even when precisely defined. This difficulty can best be overcome when information within the building industry is more freely and accurately transmitted. At present, some contractors are beginning to use the computer as a repository for cost records, and other institutions, e.g., army inventory centers, tax bureaus, and banks, are even using the computer to transmit records. Hence there is the hope that a construction estimate, based on computer-stored data, can greatly facilitate the aggregating of accurate cost data.

In sum, the designer needs a budget that must be complete and explicit before a design is made, must be a good tool for communicating with his clients, must be usable continuously throughout the term of a project, must permit the pricing of design alternatives, and must make available accurate cost information obtained from the construction industry.

5.3   Prediction

At present, in making preliminary estimates, architects first try to find budgets for existing buildings comparable with the needs, type and location of the building for their client; then they modify these budgets to meet the special conditions posed by the new problem. There are many fairly sophisticated ways for doing this sort of operation (e.g., Dow Cost Calculator,[7] using available building budgets,[10] or various appraisal systems[3, 16]). Instead of extrapolating his budget from an existing one, the architect may rely on construction-cost indexes (such as dollars per square foot, per cubic foot, or per use unit, derived from existing buildings and listed for each use type) and multiply the index against a rough estimate of the number of units his new project requires.

As has been pointed out, these systems do not adequately meet the special needs of the designer. First, though these comparative estimating systems can be used at the very outset of a project, a budget established in this manner can never be very precise and does not lend itself to detailed analysis of likely variability. Second, even at the first meeting, the client usually states requirements more specific than use, number of use units, and location, which theoretically, could permit the budget to be more precise. Budgets developed from the comparative systems are difficult to modify with specific information and cannot be modified in a continuous manner as the project becomes more precisely defined. Third, the most important purpose in early meetings is that of arriving at an explicit communication about intent; yet the comparatively derived budget cannot contain detailed information about what it includes. Further, the format of such a budget does not serve well as a device for further developing progressively a clear basis for understanding, as, say, an explicit budget list might do. Finally, a comparatively derived budget can only reflect gross levels of changes, can only very laboriously serve as a record of changes, and cannot reflect the systematic consequences of a design change or alternative.

One way of solving these problems and meeting some of the designer's special needs would be to provide, at the outset of a project, a detailed description or model of the building design. This model would have to be generated in some way from the information the client first supplies— that of *type* of building, *size* of building (usually as a function of use units), and *locale*. On the face of it this sounds like placing the paradoxical demand upon the designer that he have a detailed knowledge of his design before he has brought that design into being. However, a large amount of information exists (in the form of building codes, building customs, typical designs, planning logic, engineering requirements, market records, and so forth) from which a great deal can be "predicted" about a building before it is designed.

Alone, this fact is not of much use. If the designer has to go manually through the process of determining everything he can about his forthcoming design from this fund of knowledge, he will have to complete the design of his building (leaving out geometric and topological information) before meeting with his client for the first time. This task would take at least several weeks and surely the needs of predictive estimating would not be met.

This process would be lengthy and cumbersome because the fund of information exists in an "unordered" state as far as the design of a particular building is concerned. The pertinent parts of that information must be retrieved by the designer and processed and applied by him before being transformed into statements concerning the building he is about to design. All parts of the fund of knowledge which act as the determinants on the design must flow from the fund through the designer before affecting the description of the object he is about to design.

Licklider (Reference 13, pp. 26–28) offers a solution to this dilemma based on the use of digital computers. If the process of applying this general knowledge of buildings is thought of as a system and the fund of knowledge itself is thought of as residing in a memory (both the application system and the memory being as yet undescribed) then the use of computers will permit a *direct* connection between the fund of knowledge and the application system through which information can flow, with only a small amount of information being required by the user of the system to *direct* that flow.

Putting these ideas together then, the notion of "predictive estimating" becomes that:

1. A great deal can be determined about the design of a building without actually needing to design it.

2. A large fund of knowledge exists as the basis for making such determinations.

3. The digital computer offers a means for channeling information from this fund of knowledge through a determination process into explicit information about the forthcoming building.

An important point about this "predicted" description or model is that it would not need to be an accurate representation of the final design; it need only provide a basis for making detailed estimates at the beginning of a project. As such, it could provide the designer with a basis for explicit communication at the outset of a project. If it were possible to modify the model, on the basis of design decisions, it could be made as "accurate" as the designer's knowledge about the final design at any stage of the project. The model would then also provide a basis for continuous estimation and for gauging the effects of alternate design decisions.

5.4   Entering Descriptive Information

At first glance, having to describe a building completely sounds as hard as having to perform a quantity survey by hand. However, three facts combine to ease this task. First, the process can be a gradual one. The design of a building takes place over a period of months, and it is over this time period that the designer will input data concerning the progressing design. In fact, design data might be input in relatively small amounts as design decisions were made. Additionally, the geometry of a building changes relatively little after the preliminary design is set. The general shape of a project is determined in approximately the first 10 to 20 percent of the total time it remains in active development in the architect's office.

In a more fully developed computer system for architects, input of these data will be used for other applications than cost estimation alone. Having to enter a detailed building description for the sole purpose of cost estimation might not be worth the effort, but the description might also be used for structural and mechanical calculations, and code checking.

Third, the level of detail required for cost estimation is relatively crude. In performing a quantity takeoff, the human estimator does not use all the information contained in a set of drawings and specifications. The estimator has very little interest in the detailed dimensions and other geometric information that determine exactly where an object occurs in a building. He may wish to account for the fact that a door must be transported to the twentieth floor of a building before installation, but he is not likely to be concerned with the exact location of the door once transported, or necessarily with the extra cost of transporting it alone. Another kind of information that is not of interest to the professional estimator concerns the detailed shape of things within a building. The estimator does not much care about the exact cross-sectional shape of a window frame provided he knows its manufacturer and specification and the degree of difficulty of getting it into place.

In the latter stages of design projects, three kinds of information become available to aid in describing the design to be estimated. First is the broad class of statements that specify the materials and equipment in the building, their locations, and sometimes their quantities. Second is geometric information to serve as a basis for calculating the quantities of materials and other items and to serve as a frame of reference within which to make statements about them. Third is information, sometimes only implied, concerning the quality of the material and type of joinery involved in placing it.

These three classes of data—materials and quantities, geometry, and qualities—are presently described to the estimator in plans and specifications. The designer draws up graphic and text documents; the graphic ones indicate the geometry and hence quantities of the materials in the proposed project and act as a map to locate materials and details; the text documents (specifications) and some of the material in the graphic documents (details, notes, schedules) indicate the qualities and further definition of the quantities of materials. The process of compiling the list of materials from such documents requires much human skill in interpreting the documents and much time-consuming manual effort in putting the information into the proper forms for mathematical manipulations. A computer-aided estimation process might be based on entering information concerning the building into a computer file; the computer would then operate on this file of information to perform an operation similar to the takeoff process.

This file of information about the building might initially be built up by the prediction progress suggested in the last section, and then *modified,* as the design progressed, by descriptive information entered by the architect. The fact that information will be entered slowly, as the design proceeds, suggests that it may be entered independently of the process of encoding it into contract documents. Thus the approach to entering information for estimates might be based on a new system for describing buildings rather than by decoding information from the traditional contract documents.

Two ways are available to enter geometric information. The most direct way would be by means of graphic devices such as the light pen or the "Grafacon" tracing device discussed by Clark (Reference 4, p. 22). However, during the design of a project there is a long period in which the basic layout does not change (or, if it does change, changes in a way that can be dealt with by means of *statements* rather than graphic input). This suggests that input of geometric data by means of numerical coordinates can be a feasible approach. In this instance, typewriters or teletypewriters could be used to provide "feedback" plans of sufficient detail to check the accuracy of input data. Because there is a great likelihood that sophisticated, graphic devices will become available, they could well be used for cost estimating, even though they are not essential for it.

Entry of the names and locations of materials and equipment might be accomplished by text statements, in a carefully designed communication language. The form and vocabulary of the language should match as closely as possible the "natural" ways in which designers describe buildings. Because a large amount of information would need to be entered to describe a building, the language should provide a means for ensuring the consistency and completeness of the information. In part, this could be accomplished by providing a means for retrieval of information in the file. In addition, there should be a means for detecting and noting inconsistent statements. A third feature might be a checklist facility to help ensure completeness.

Entering geometric information and information about materials and equipment appears to be straightforward. By contrast, information concerning the quality and difficulties of construction is less readily entered.

Much cost-affecting information is embodied in architectural details. Though direct graphic input of architectural detail drawings appears theoretically possible, the process poses practical problems at present. Furthermore, even if this information could be entered, the problem of analyzing it to extract cost information does not seem readily solvable, because of the lack of standardization in the ways details are presented graphically (Clark, Reference 4, p. 5).

One solution to this problem might be based on the fact that construction cost is heavily dependent upon the way materials are *joined* together. Building parts are made of materials and joints. For example, a paint is "joined" to a wall in one, two, or three coats; a concrete mix is set into place with differing degrees of care and costs of handling; and a wood stud is "joined" to the sill and plate in a less careful manner than a piece of 2 by 4 millwork in an exposed screen wall. The labor of placing the stud or screen element could be said to be embodied in the joints. One way to handle the information in architectural details might be to develop a consistent language of joinery. Using this approach, a detail would be "entered" by stating the materials and their amounts, and the *amount* and *quality* of the joints. The success of this approach would depend on a consistent way of describing joint quantities and a scale for their qualities.

Another kind of information that affects cost is the quality of finishes, tolerances of construction, and special construction techniques that are implied or described in drawings and specifications. As in the case of architectural details, this kind of information is not standardized, and its precise effect on cost is difficult to determine analytically. As with architectural details, it might be possible to develop special codings of such information in order to input qualitative information. However, one solution to both these problems that reflects present-day practice is the exercise of human judgment. Allowing for ways to permit "human judgment" could provide a means for dealing with any information at present too complex to be coded economically into a form permitting it to become an automatic part of the system.

The first and simplest way to permit judgment would be to allow the user to enter unit costs directly in place of those supplied by the system. A second tool for allowing the exercise of judgment would be an index system that would affect the data in complex and thorough ways, even though it appeared simple to the user. Such a system might enable the infrequent user to develop a high degree of skill at exercising his "judgment." This is especially important because, though the computer can handle much information in a precise way, the system will produce results accurate only to the degree that skill can be aggregated in building up that system, combined with the skill with which the system is used.

Indexes can generally be applied in two ways, either against estimate totals or else at appropriate points throughout the system. The former is the least accurate, easiest, and possibly the only meaningful way to apply certain indexes. A more elaborate form of index might apply with a different weighting to each appropriate place it is applied. One form of such an index might carry a selective range of applications, a "value profile," that makes the index affect each variable an appropriate amount, much as a key moves tumblers. Presently, systems exist for deriving a cost index to modify certain lists of basic costs—for example, to modify material averages for a locale, to modify large-quantity prices for small purchases, or to modify present prices in accord with statistical projections for prices in effect during future construction.[6] There are other factors to which professional estimators pay special attention and which they handle in a way comparable with that of using "subjective" indexes. Some of these are the reputation of the client, the reputation of the architect, the reputation of the contractor, the status of the market, and the general quality of the construction proposed. The development of an index for each of these is possible; political and economic factors will govern whether such developments are desirable or feasible.

Besides providing means for modifying inputs by means of indexes, indications of possible variability within the estimate produced would aid the user in exercising his judgment.

5.5   Cost Calculation

The last two sections have developed the idea of a computer-stored description of a building as central to a computer-aided estimating system. To obtain an estimate based on the information in this description, two additional elements would be required: a source, or "library," of cost information and a process which would combine the stored building description with the cost information to calculate the estimated cost of the building. This process would perform the equivalent of a material takeoff and cost calculation and would produce tabulated outputs equivalent to those obtained from estimators.

Costs for the items in the stored building description could be established in several ways. Since the system would contain a library of costs and a means for establishing references between it and the stored building description, costs could be established automatically at the time information about the building was entered into the system. In making design decisions, the architect could also review materials and their costs brought forth from the library. As suggested earlier, the architect could override automatic cost selection by entering unit costs manually. Finally, he could modify established costs in the system by entering cost multipliers, or indexes. The processes would be applicable to predicted design information as well as information entered by the architect.

The comprehensibility of the system to the user will affect its utility to him. One of the most important factors in the takeoff process is the form in which the material is presented; indeed the available formats of the printed output will embody the meaning of the system. The question of the form of the output is essentially a "political" one. Since it has been assumed that the computer-based estimating system will be relied upon by all the parties engaged in the construction industry, the print-out should be meaningful to all of them. However, the two principal users, architects and contractors, have very different interests in how the costs of the building are broken down. Though there may be only one stored building model and one cost-data bank, there should be at least two forms of takeoffs.

The architect, especially at the early stages of his design (and generally when he must interpret information to his client), wishes to see the cost of a material related to use units such as the spaces or "enclosure elements" (e.g., cost of one flooring material in the circulation spaces versus cost of a second material in a utility space) as opposed to the total cost of a material summed up from wherever it occurs. Second, he wishes to have the categories for cost breakdowns be in terms of functional units (i.e., in terms of spaces, enclosure elements, or equipment) rather than breakdowns by trades. Third, architects are interested not only in what material is in the estimate but also in what alternate materials exist for a given application at the same price or at different prices, and what are their different performance characteristics, maintenance costs, etc.

Since the formats for existing construction estimating systems have been developed by contractors or professionals oriented to the needs of contractors, architects have more of a problem developing formats than do contractors. The question of what format to provide for general contractors is straightforward because the trade has already developed formats of its own. Generally speaking, estimates are broken down by the trades involved. Because of the structure of the industry (given such factors as union practices) contractors all tend to use the same or similar formats.*

Possibly the greatest advantage in having a building description stored in computer form is that the consequences of any alteration to the description could be computed. Because the description contains a reference to cost, the effect on cost of any descriptive change could be studied.† Hence, just as the computer is proving to be a tool for studying mechanical

* For example, the Construction Specifications Institute, in developing a format for architectural specifications, followed a "consensus" breakdown of contractor estimates so that the contractor could follow the architect's specifications in an orderly manner while reflecting them in his breakdown of costs. The CSI breakdown has sixteen separate sections; actual breakdowns submitted by various different contractors showed close coincidence to this format—differences tending to be only omissions or additions of sections as individual jobs demanded.

† A sophisticated system would permit the designer to vary items which affect cost in complex ways, such as changing dimensions of structural members automatically while taking into account changes in floor and wall area.

and structural systems, it may also prove to be of value in studying cost consequences. Because the model proposed would always be complete, whether or not its parts were predicted or described, a change in cost could always be reflected for any part, and the increment or difference in total noted. Thus the system could become a design tool.

One of the worst communication breakdowns between persons in discussing an estimate is what has or has not been included in it. This stems from the fact that architects and contractors use different inventory-list breakdowns and add different overhead profit and contingency factors to the various total quantities. A computer-based estimating system must therefore ensure that its users understand its formats and could usefully print explicitly the overriding assumptions. Two classes of information could usefully accompany the output of estimated cost to give the user an indication of the accuracy of the information provided. They are indications of completeness and indications of the degree of variability to be expected.

Variability in the estimate can be a function of first, uncertainties *in the mind of the user;* second, cost instability or variance of costs *in the construction field;* and third, the relative sensitivity or insensitivity of measures *in the estimating system.* Since each dimension of variability occurs in a physically different area, each dimension should be handled in a separate manner. A number of methods might be built into a computer-based estimating system to indicate to the user the variability caused by his uncertainties.

First, records of how accurate a predicted estimate is at the various stages of design could be analyzed. Second, an indication could be provided as to whether a predicted item was selected randomly, selected as having high probability, by the prediction process, or was subject to great variance in the future. Third, a simple index to aid the user in eliminating the more important uncertainties in his mind could be obtained by indicating beside each item in the estimate what percent of the total cost that item comprised.

Variance in costs in the construction field comes from numerous and complex factors; hence, instead of trying for accuracy by simulating all the possible interactions in the field, it might be more meaningful to indicate the range of the variance to be expected in an estimate. Unlike a printed list of costs, a computer-based cost library could be continually modified, and the statistical calculations necessary to develop indications of variability might therefore be practical to perform. The information that could be used for deriving measures of variability would be the number of price choices in a category and the range of prices that occur.

Overall, accuracy of the system will improve as total cost is calculated because aggregated costs are more accurate than disaggregated ones. Besides having measures of probability of particular cost figures, a measure can be developed to gauge the accuracy of an estimate total through utilization of well-known statistical techniques. Without further development, it is extremely difficult to predict the amount of data needed to form the various indications of variability. One can only say that, as is true of the rest of the procedure in developing this computer-based estimating system, the cost of getting information would have to be weighed against the value of providing that information.

5.6   Unit-cost Library

A major problem for the designer today is that of getting accurate construction costs. Because the process of getting unit costs is one which is affected by every aspect of the construction marketplace, architects (and contractors) spend a good deal of time working with difficult communication problems that procuring unit costs entails. Typically, architectural offices have handbooks, manufacturers' prices, and usually disorganized, outdated, and incomplete data from previous projects. Handbooks give skimpy information and need large multipliers to make them accurate; manufacturers' prices contain a good deal of wishful thinking and generally are not consistently arranged, especially with respect to labor costs or contractors' overhead and profit; and finally, the architects' records usually cannot be revised, even when located, to adjust accurately from the context of the old project to that of the new.

The ultimate source for costs is the actual construction operation. However, the architect is not usually interested in *construction* costs but rather in the costs of material in place. The designer's task is to develop the specifications for a physical product—not for the process of erecting that product. This is most apparent in the documents an architect issues— these describe products in place, not the process of putting them there. One way to develop an accurate and useful data bank of costs would be to develop a system to transform costs based on construction processes into costs of units in place.

There are three methods for converting from process-based construction costs to in-place costs: the first could be for architects to phrase their documents in terms of construction processes instead of a finished building; the second would be an automatic system to provide an interface between a design description and the construction process; and a third would be to compile in-place costs directly from process costs.

The problem of having designers convert their documents into explicit construction-process information is both a political and technical one. Technically, it would mean giving the architects a new vocabulary with which to communicate processes. This would not meet their present needs for communicating with clients as well as contractors and would involve extensive retraining. Presently, there is some pressure in the other direction, i.e., to write a description of performance, leaving the contractor to designate a construction solution and then a process for achieving it. But, by allowing the inference of construction process to be handled automatically, the option of architects to describe the products in place could still be considered.

The problem of automatically interfacing design descriptions to process descriptions has been partly solved. In the COBESTCO[12] study the parts of a building were decomposed into their constituent processes by means of the critical-path network. In using this device, human judgment is employed in determining just how building parts break down into construction processes. Once the construction processes have been determined, a combination of human judgment, calculation, and stored historic records is used to determine how much labor, material and equipment of each sort will go into each process. Hence, the interface between the two descriptions has been developed by manual techniques; human judgment still provides the necessary link.

Automating this process may be the ultimate way to build up a continuous costing system and design tool; but for the present, there are some advantages to staying with a simple solution. Consequently, it is suggested that the cost library be based on the third approach—converting construction costs to in-place costs.

The cost library would be a catalog of the cost of materials and of various systems of joining them. The unit costs in the library would consist of three basic parts—the unit cost of each *material,* and the cost of joining the materials, which breaks down into the wage rate for each kind of *labor* required and the rate of cost for each kind of *equipment* employed.

The above are basic rates for labor, equipment, and materials independent of their particular application. In addition, it would be necessary to state *how much* of each of the above "ingredients" was necessary for a given in-place unit. Thus three more pieces of information would be required: the productivity of each kind of labor when doing a particular kind of job, the amount of each material required per unit of the item being measured, and the productivity of each kind of equipment for that application.

Hence there are six variables to keep track of in all: a statement of cost of a unit of material, labor, or equipment, and an appropriate rate for each type of material, labor, or equipment necessary to put one unit in place. Such a list of relationships can be contained either in handbooks (e.g., Means,[9]) listing all possible combinations (at least the commonest ones) or in ones listing costs[6,15,16] of units and the rules for what rates to apply in combining the prices. To obtain these costs, the following information must be collected: wage rates, costs of materials and information for determining productivity, and other cost ratios. Periodically these raw data would be subjected to a statistical-analysis process that would produce single-number values for each wage, productivity, etc. These values would then be inserted into the cost library and the various in-place unit costs updated.

There are a number of limitations to any standard library of cost information. Two problems concern interdependencies between the items in a building. One of these is dependency of the in-place cost of an item upon *its location* in the building. An outside block wall may cost more than an inside block partition because of the cost of the required scaffolding. A block partition on the fortieth floor may cost more than one on the first floor because of the cost of transporting laborers, equipment, and materials to the fortieth floor. Also of concern is the dependency of cost upon the *way an item is used.* For example, metal lath and plaster may cost three different amounts when used over masonry, wood studs, or as a suspended ceiling.

There are two criteria for solving these problems. First, the degree of differentiation can be determined only by finding what the cost of achieving an additional step is and what is the value of doing so. This question can be answered only in terms of a survey of the commercial needs and potentials for the whole system. Second, no cost differentiation is valuable unless there is also an instruction from the makeup of the model which makes distinctions that can utilize the cost differential.

As discussed earlier, the estimation process appears to be inherently dependent on human judgment, and it is concerning just such problems as the ones discussed above that judgment is much used in the human estimating process. Therefore, a likely solution is to treat the problems above in part as basic limitations of a standard cost library, and to rely on manual override, as discussed earlier, in the form of manual insertion of unit costs or cost indexes.

5.7 A Computer System for Cost Estimating: External Aspects for Architects

Physically, the system might consist of a teletypewriter and possibly one or more graphical input-output devices located in the designer's office and connected to a remotely located, time-shared computer. The user would be able to type in statements, questions, and commands, enter graphic information, and receive output statements and tabulation via the tele-typewriter. A well-designed language would be provided enabling the user to make statements in the vocabulary he naturally uses when describing buildings. He could also enter drawings and view displays of the information he had entered.

At the outset of a project, the user would state the type, size (in "use" units), and location of his project to the system. For example, he might type:

Grade school, 300 pupils, northeast semiurban

Based on this minimum information and a body of stored background information, the system would generate a file of "predicted" information concerning the forthcoming project.

To the user of the system, this file would resemble a "model" of the project he is about to undertake. The file would contain explicit information about the spaces, materials, and equipment in the building. The designer could request tabulations of information concerning the predicted building, and of its cost. He could also replace predicted information within the file by statements describing the building.

This file would provide a basis for early cost estimating. Because it would contain explicit and detailed information about the expected contents of the eventual building, it would aid accurate communication with the client and help to minimize misunderstandings about the building budget. Because the information in this file could be replaced by the designer, it would also serve as a device for testing design assumptions for their cost, for making explicit the cost consequences of design decisions, and for keeping a record of budget changes.

As the project progressed, definite design decisions would be made and entered. The information in these incoming descriptive statements would replace former predicted information in the stored file. An important point is that, though the stored file would always be in process of modification, it would always be *complete*. This completeness would allow for *continuous,* or *incremental,* estimating—the estimated cost of the project could be determined, if desired, after each design decision. Moreover, the designer could use the system as a tool to evaluate different kinds of alternate design decisions. He could try different materials for all corridor walls, for example, obtaining revised cost estimates for each; and of greater importance, he could determine the effect on cost of geometric changes (for example, the basic structural grid spacing) without needing to state explicitly their consequences, such as changes in wall and floor areas.

A key part of the system would be a process to perform quantity take-offs from the stored design information. Generally, however, the designer would not need to concern himself with quantities when *entering* information; he would have only to describe the building in a way natural to him.

Alternate takeoff formats would group materials into units of interest to the designer—use units, spaces, enclosure, elements, etc.—or to the contractor—breakdown by trade, type of material, and application. Along with takeoff tabulations, the system could provide special indications, such as the percentage of the total cost represented by a given part or ranges of materials applicable to a given use.

The system would contain a library of unit-cost information, derived directly from construction records. Estimates produced by the system could be based on unit-cost information from the stored library or on unit costs supplied directly by the designer. He could also supply cost multipliers or indexes affecting the costs of whole groups of materials or of the entire building.

The dominant characteristic of the system and its chief value to the user would be as an organizer of information. The system would not be dominated by any large, single operation; rather, it would contain a large number of small operations tying together several bodies of data.

5.8   Structure of the System

The computer system has been summarized as it might be seen by a user. In order to see how it might accomplish the tasks we have outlined, we must examine its internal structure.* Figure 5.1 shows the system as we see it. Rectangular blocks represent processes to transform the information; arrows represent the flow of information in the system.

Central to the scheme is a body of data entitled "building model," which contains a description of the user's current project. Two other files contain auxiliary information. One contains a body of data used to assemble a "predicted" building description on the basis of broad, general statements at the beginning of a project. A second auxiliary file contains a library of unit costs which, in conjunction with the building file, provides automatic estimates.

Several processes link these bodies of data. Two of these accept general building information and insert it into the two auxiliary files—the cost library and the predictive information file. Two main input processes are available to the user. One of these accepts "general" statements from the

---

* The system's structure is summarized briefly here; for a more detailed description, see the report upon which this chapter is based.

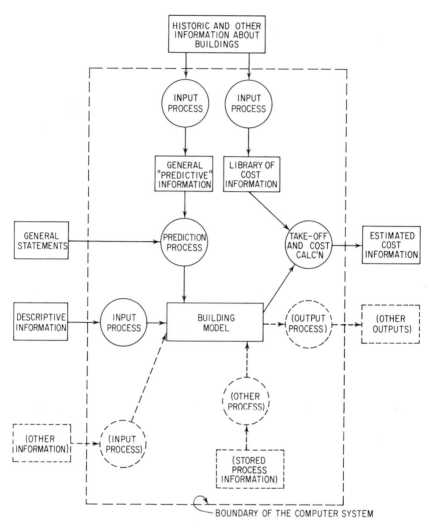

Fig. 5.1 Overall structure of the system

user and on their basis channels information from the file of predictive information into the building file. This process has the effect of generating predicted building images. A second input process accepts specific descriptive statements and inserts them directly into the building description, modifying or replacing the data already there as appropriate.

A second major process in the system has the task of operating on the building description to calculate its cost. This process performs the equivalent of quantity takeoff, and combines the result with unit costs drawn from the cost library, or entered by the user, to calculate the total cost of the building. The process also accepts and applies special measures such as range of choices and sensitivity of building price to a given item.

In a working system, an executive process would channel information from the user to the several input processes, and maintain overall control of the system on the basis of user commands. However, the nature of the executive process is not important in the present discussion.

The building file would be the keystone for the rest of the system. For the system to function effectively, it should fulfill several goals. It must, of course, contain sufficient information about the materials and equipment, their relationships and locations, to permit cost estimation. More importantly, its organization should let the user enter design information, ask questions about the building, and specify design changes in as natural a way as possible. One way to do this would be to design a file system whose structure could reflect the physical structure of a building and could grow and change in response to the changing design.

A file organized to suit the designer would not necessarily lend itself naturally to cost estimation. For the purposes of estimation, one would want a file that aggregated building information by material. This goal could be achieved without sacrificing utility to the designer if one could design a file system in which more than one organizing structure would be superimposed upon the same body of information.

A technique for organizing information in computers known as list structuring appears to meet these several goals and seems well suited as a basis for the building file. It permits highly complex data structures to be formed in computer memory, allows these structures to grow and change over time, and allows multiple structures to be superimposed over a single body of information.

One can describe list-structured files in terms of the actual organization of computer memory. Without resorting to computer technology, one can also describe such files graphically as networks formed of the actual elements to be stored and their relationships.

In such a network, the *entities* to be stored form the nodes; relationships, known as *attributes,* between the entities link the nodes together. For example, as shown below, the entities "wall" and "plaster" are said to

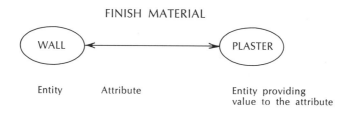

FINISH MATERIAL

| Entity | Attribute | Entity providing value to the attribute |

provide a *value* to the attribute "finish material" of the wall. Entities stand for the many things such as walls, spaces, doorknobs, and electrical junction boxes that make up a building. Attributes stand for the many relationships between these things, lend structure to the building file, and allow it to reflect the physical structure of the actual building.

Figure 5.2 shows how an actual (but greatly simplified) building might be described by a network of entities and attributes. Certain attributes allow the network to represent explicitly the topology of the building. For example, space S1 is to the west of space S2, and the two are separated by a wall. Other attributes express the relation of ownership.[4] For example, each space "owns" a ceiling and a floor. A wall may "own" doors and windows.

For clarity, many attributes and entities have been omitted from the figure; a fully developed network would contain other entities and attributes providing numerical geometric information, information about materials, finishes, and equipment, etc.

Note that the ouside walls of the building are tied together by a dotted line. These entities are said to belong to a set, in this case the set of all outside walls. The set relationship is useful for tying together similar entities that are not related by attributes.

5.9 Communicating with the System

A key part of the system is the language in which the user would communicate with it. The communication language might be based on the notation discussed in the last section. Most descriptive statements one can make about a building involve the value of an attribute of an entity. For example, in the statement "the outside walls are brick," an *entity* "outside walls" is referred to; an *attribute* "material" is implied by the word "are," and the attribute is given the *value* "brick." Thus the typical statement might contain three elements: an entity, an attribute, and a second entity serving as the value of the attribute. An additional element (implicit or explicit) would be needed to indicate *action*. The following actions are possible: an attribute can be created or removed; an attribute value can be created, removed, or changed. Thus, one might say:

"Remove the roof from the building."
(Action: remove; Entity: building;
Attribute: ownership; Value: roof)

"Change the outside walls from concrete block to brick."
"Put a skylight on the roof."

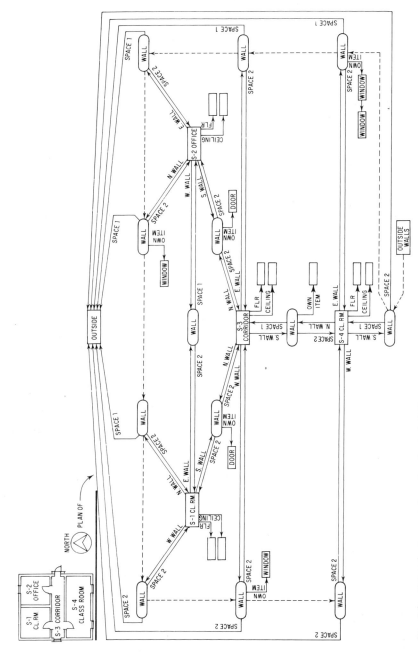

Fig. 5.2 Network representation of a simple building

"The wall has two windows."

(Action implied: Give the wall two windows)

To build up a complete building description using statements such as these would require some way of linking them into a *structure*. The key lies in the fact that an attribute value is itself an entity. Thus, in the first statement above, "roof" was treated as a value, in the third as an entity. Using this idea, one can rapidly build up a fairly complex structure:

"The building has three classrooms."

"The classroom has an outside wall."

"The wall has a door."

"The door has a knob."

"The knob is made of machined bronze."

To be more powerful, statements of this kind could be made applicable to *sets* of entities:

"The classrooms have windows."

To make specification of entity easier, *complex* specifications should be allowed:

"The north wall of the corridor of the south wing has lockers."

This general form of statement could also be used to enter unit costs and indexes:

"The bookcases in the classroom have a unit cost of $40 per linear foot."

The above is a suggestion of approach only; further investigation would be required to determine whether statements of this sort are a convenient way to describe buildings. However, in terms of implementation, this vocabulary could definitely be used to build up complex networks using a simple input program. The key here is that the form of the vocabulary is close to the form of the network to be assembled.

Queries about information in the system could be built on the same structure used for input. The only difference would be that the *action* components of queries would be "type" or "print." For example:

"Type the basic material of the outside walls."

Two kinds of higher-level commands would be useful. One kind would output whole classes or sections of stored information:

"Type the materials and locations of the walls."

Some commands would require *calculation* in addition to retrieval:

"Type the volume of concrete in the building."

Another desirable component of the language would be some form of feedback to ensure that input was consistent with information already stored. This might take the form of a dialogue, with machine statements in the form of complaints or queries:

(User)   "There is a 5- by 10-foot sliding glass door in the north wall of classroom 10."

(Machine) "The north wall of classroom 10 is 8 feet high."

The descriptive statements discussed above contain four basic components: an entity or set of entities, an attribute, the value of an attribute, and the action to be taken. The input process would handle these statements by extracting the four components, finding the entity to be acted on, and manipulating the structure of the file to achieve the desired action.

5.10   Prediction Process

At the outset of the estimating process, information is generated which represents a "predicted" description of the project about to be designed. The concept behind this scheme was discussed in Sec. 5.2. Prediction would depend on a body of background information and a procedure for extracting from this information predicted descriptions of buildings. The problem, as it appears to us, is to achieve a reasonably compact body of background data while allowing a usefully fine-grained range of possible predicted images.

A relatively compact body of data might be possible because diverse buildings generally have much in common. In general, different buildings are built of common parts; different parts are often constructed using the same vocabulary or subparts. This fact would be taken advantage of in organizing the data. In general, "typical" items would be stored once and referred to by the various higher-level items that can "own" them.

Processes in the system would interact with the data in various ways to generate specific building images. In general, processes would *quantify* and *select*. For example, one kind of process might compute the expected number of spaces in a building on the basis of its size (in use units). Another process might select the kind of structural system for a building on the basis of its size and location.

Input statements would serve in part as indexes to retrieve information, in part as parameters for processes embedded in the data. For example, at the highest level of the structure, the entity "grade school" might have among its attributes "classroom" and "possible structural systems." It would also have, as attributes, processes to compute the number of classrooms and select a structural system. Entry of the statement "grade school" would cause selection of that entity from the set of possible building types. The information "300 pupils" would serve as a basis for calculating the number of classrooms expected.

So far we have treated the prediction process as something that happens once at the beginning of a project, and assumed that all input statements after the first would contain specific, descriptive information. In actual fact, statements would fall in a continuum ranging from general to specific, and all statements but the most specific would need to be augmented by predicted information. Thus the statement "the building has a concrete structural system" tells more than a specification of type and size but does not contain the kind of information needed for a quantity takeoff. It would be necessary to devise mechanisms to generate varying amounts of predicted information in response to statements on different levels and to insert this information into the file.

5.11 Takeoff and Cost Calculation

This process would combine information in the building file with information in the cost library to obtain the estimated cost of the building.

We envision list structuring as being applied to the cost library as well as the building file. Each material or assembly of materials would have three sets of attributes, one each for the labor, materials, and equipment that are needed to put it in place. Each labor, equipment, and material would, in turn, have two attributes, a basic cost and a rate of use or productivity. Figure 5.3 shows how the cost library might be structured.

The cost library might serve as a master inventory of possible building parts linked directly to information in the building file. For example, the in-place items in the cost library could serve as attribute values for entities in the building file. This approach is illustrated in Fig. 5.4.

The information in architectural drawings is organized in a way that describes buildings clearly but is not well suited to the takeoff process. This difficulty could be overcome in a list-structured data file by using more than one organizing structure. The basic structure makes the data appear as a model or description of a building. Superimposed over this could be a second structure more appropriate to the intent of the takeoff procedure.

For example, entities in the building file could be linked into sets by material, with each set originating at the appropriate entry in the cost library. Thus at the "8-inch concrete block" entry in the library would be accessible all parts of the building constructed of that material. The takeoff process could then be based on a search through the cost library.

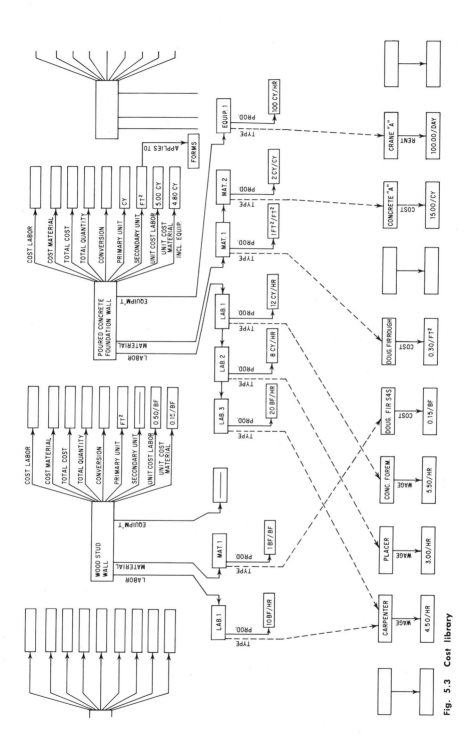

Fig. 5.3 Cost library

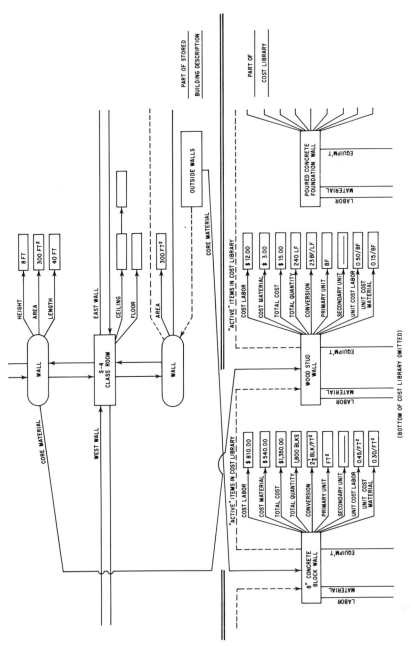

Fig. 5.4 Cost library as a reference to the stored building description

Differences between takeoff formats amount to different partitions of the contents of a building. Thus the contractor's format is equivalent to a partition of the building parts by trades, whereas a format relevant to designers might be based on a partition by components, such as walls and floors. In general, any number of partitions could be achieved by linking items in the building model into different sets, and different partitions could exist simultaneously.

The actual cost calculation would be a straightforward arithmetic operation involving application of unit costs to calculated quantities, totaling, and applying measures (possibly entered by the user) to total costs to account for labor, benefits, profit, etc.

Incremental estimating would depend on accounting for the effect on cost of each change to the building file. This could be done by accounting for each change separately or repeating the entire takeoff operation each time a new estimate was demanded.

5.12   Practical Implications

Realization of the system sketched here depends on overcoming technical and political difficulties.

The estimating system should be as accessible to the designer as possible, both physically and in terms of time. Immediate access could be achieved with a small, inexpensive computer, or through time sharing. One factor that points to time sharing is the desirability of extensive background information, such as a frequently updated cost library. Compiling such a library would probably be beyond the means of the single user and would probably require some form of central data file. Commercial, general-purpose time-sharing systems are presently rare but are becoming more available.

Judging from the amount of *information* that would be required for a stored building description and a workable cost library (Clark, Reference 4, p. 38), these two bodies of data would exceed presently available core-memory capacities. In addition, because the system is to be based on list processing in combination with large amounts of data, processing speed might be too slow to permit very immediate response to user commands. However, higher-speed list-processing systems are under development and core-memory sizes and speeds are both increasing. If the approaches suggested in this chapter are feasible, the present limitations imposed by hardware may cease to be problems within the next few years.

In preparing construction estimates, most contractors use private catalogs of in-place unit costs derived from their own construction records.

This leads to the problem of making an estimating system based on "standard" unit costs as useful to contractors as their personal records are. Similarly, while it would be desirable to avoid the discontinuity between the architect's final estimate and the contractor's estimate, it is doubtful that contractors would readily assume responsibility for meeting an unfamiliar machine-generated estimate.

Building a cost library also presents political problems because the construction industry is highly competitive, with much to be gained by secrecy. Contractors and professional estimators regard their cost libraries as proprietary information. Manufacturers are willing to quote prices privately but are reticent to publish them. Moreover, the estimates given tend to lack an indication of the scope of work included.

However, architects exert a certain amount of control over the construction market. Hence, if architects were to use a computer system for estimating, there is the hope that the form in which information is needed might encourage the provision of more uniform, accurate, and readily accessible information.

5.13 Conclusion

This chapter has defined the needs of an architectural designer for cost estimating and has discussed the requirements of a computer-based estimating system that would meet these needs. The proposed system has four parts: first, a computer-based model would be predicted when little specific information about a project was known; second, descriptive information would gradually be inserted into the model as design decisions were made; third, the costs would be calculated, totaled, and printed out in appropriate formats, possibly with an indication of the invariability; and fourth, a cost library would be developed independently from any specific project as a source of costs to be applied against the computer-based building description.

The system appears to have several advantages over existing techniques:

1. It would permit estimates based on explicit, detailed information early in the course of a project.

2. Because this information is gradually modified during the course of a project, it would serve as a basis for continuous, incremental estimating.

3. The tedious, time-consuming, and expensive takeoff process would be performed by machine.

4. Because of automated takeoffs, the system might permit more frequent alternate estimates than now possible.

5. Estimates could be based on unit costs derived explicitly from construction records.

6. Broadly, much of the present burden of organization and keeping track of information would be removed from the designer.

This approach has several potential problems, and approaches for overcoming these have been discussed:

1. A "predicted" building design suffers from the inherent unlikelihood that it is an accurate prediction of what will be built. Three factors lessen the effect of this problem. First, there is no reason why a cost estimate based on a detailed, predicted breakdown should be less accurate than an estimate based on the measured, per-square-foot cost of an existing building (which in itself implies a detailed prediction of the building to be designed). Besides, the need at this earliest stage of estimation is for an explicit model to serve as the basis for designing as well as for an accurate prediction of what the undesigned building will cost. Second, a more detailed study of this problem of prediction may reveal more sophisticated techniques which improve the effective accuracy of predicted building designs. Finally, if the machine system permits the appropriate exercise of human judgment, its results can be no worse than the present practices.

2. The task of completely describing a building is a difficult one. However, as discussed elsewhere, the process is made easier by the fact that it is gradual, by the provision of a well-designed input language, and (indirectly) by the fact that the information put in can be used for other purposes than cost estimating.

3. Good cost estimating depends on skill and a "deep" knowledge of the construction process, and we have not been able to see any ways of replacing these human characteristics by an automatic process. However, we feel this problem can be overcome by giving the human user of the system an easy mechanism for overriding its automatic operation through the device of manually input costs and cost indexes, and a way of judging the estimates through indications of variability.

While this chapter has concerned cost estimating it should be borne in mind that this is but one of the architect's tasks. Any computer system to help cost estimating would be more valuable if it were part of a larger system to aid the entire architectural process. A key aspect of that process is communication; the architect must communicate with a broad range of people in the building industry. The computer promises to help communication in two ways: by providing a single, up-to-date repository of information about a project accessible to all involved with the project; and by serving as a mechanism for the *transmission* as well as storage of information.

The computer's impact on communication may in turn have its effects on the establishment and dissemination of costs in the construction industry. By providing a two-way communication path—cost information to architects, design information to manufacturers and contractors—the computer may eventually become the marketplace for the construction industry.

REFERENCES

1. *Quality Standards of the Architectural Woodwork Industry,* Architectural Woodwork Institute, Nashville, Tenn., 1963.
2. D. G. Bobrow, "Natural Language Input for a Computer Problem Solving System," *M.I.T. Project MAC Technical Report TR-1,* September, 1964.
3. E. H. Boeckh, *Manual of Appraisals,* The Rough Notes Co., Inc., Indianapolis, Ind., 1934.
4. Bolt, Beranek and Newman, Inc., "Computer-aided Checking of Design Documents for Compliance with Regulatory Codes," *Report* 1260, Job 163434, July, 1965.
5. *The CSI Format for Construction Specifications,* The Construction Specification Institute, Washington, D.C., 1964.
6. L. Dallavia, *Estimating General Construction Costs,* F. W. Dodge Company, a Division of McGraw-Hill, Inc., New York, 1957.
7. *Dow Building Cost Calculator and Valuation Guide,* F. W. Dodge Company, a Division of McGraw-Hill, Inc., New York, 1964.
8. *Computer Language for Architectural Specifications (CLASP),* Fair-Isaac and Co., San Rafael, Calif., 1965.
9. R. S. Godfrey (ed.), *Building Construction Cost Data,* Robert S. Means Co., Duxbury, Mass., 1942.
10. Joint Committee on Building Costs, *Building Cost Manual,* John Wiley & Sons, Inc., New York, 1957.
11. J. Kemeny, A. Schleiffer, Jr., J. Laurie Snell, and G. L. Thompson, *Finite Mathematics with Business Applications,* Prentice-Hall, Inc., Englewood Cliffs, N.J., 1962.
12. P. Kramer and L. R. Shaffer, *COBESTCO (Computer-based Estimating Technique for Contractors),* Civil Engineering Studies, Construction Research Series no. 7, Report of Civil Engineering, University of Illinois, Urbana, Ill., February, 1965.
13. J. C. R. Licklider, *Libraries of the Future,* The M.I.T. Press, Cambridge, Mass., 1965.
14. W. H. Linder, *Mathematical Object Description Language,* Civil Engineering Systems Laboratory, M.I.T. Department of Civil Engineering, 1965.
15. J. S. Page, *Estimators General Construction Man-hour Manual,* Gulf Press, New York, 1959.
16. H. E. Pulver, *Construction Estimates and Costs,* 3d ed., McGraw-Hill Book Company, New York, 1960.
17. D. Roos and B. Schumacher, *ICES: Integrated Civil Engineering System,* M.I.T. Department of Civil Engineering, 1965.
18. J. J. Souder, *Estimating Space Needs and Costs in General Hospital Construction,* American Hospital Association, Chicago, 1963.

CHAPTER SIX *Accounting*

By Richard C. La Velle

The problem of the method of accounting and job-control information needed to manage a professional office is one that has occupied countless hours of top-management time. Whether the information is produced by hand or machine, it must be incisive, timely, and accurate. An outline of a basic accounting and job-control system which meets these requirements for a typical professional office is presented in the pages that follow.

Mr. La Velle is a manager within the Administrative Services Division of Arthur Andersen & Co. He holds a B.S. degree in Commerce from the State University of Iowa. His work consists of assisting clients in all phases of accounting and information-systems development. This includes feasibility studies, systems design, and systems implementation.

6.1 The Basic Functions and Requirements of Accounting

Our economic system revolves around the profit motive, and this is as true in professional architecture and engineering firms as it is in retail stores or manufacturing companies. Perhaps the most basic function of accounting is to maintain records of the firm's operations so that the net income or loss for a specific period may be measured. This requires the prompt and accurate recording of the day-to-day transactions of the business. Furthermore, during the course of a firm's operations, the composition of the assets and equities in such assets change. The accounting records must reflect these changes and be able to produce timely information to the firm's management so that they can control their business. In addition, such information is usually required by banks and other financial institutions when a firm finances a part of the business through borrowing.

6.2 The Accounting Method

A firm can maintain its records and report income or loss on a cash basis or on an accrual basis of accounting. When records are maintained on a cash basis, "income . . . is regarded as earned in the period in which the cash collection is received. . . . Expenses are regarded as applicable to the period in which cash payment is made. . . . On the accrual basis of accounting, income is taken up in the period in which it is earned by sales or services (regardless of when collected), and expenses are charged to income in the period in which they are incurred (regardless of when paid)."[1] The accrual method matches income and expense in the appropriate accounting period, which provides management with a better tool to evaluate past performance and plan future operations.

A firm may also elect to report income or loss on a completed-contract or on a percentage-of-completion basis. In a sense, the completed-contract method is similar to the cash basis of accounting in that income or loss is reported in the period in which the contract is completed. The percentage-of-completion method presumes revenues are earned as the work progresses, and the expenses are charged against such revenues to determine income or loss. The percentage-of-completion method, like the accrual basis of accounting, has the advantage of matching income and expenses in an accounting period. This information can be evaluated in relation to past accounting periods and in relation to the financial plan established by management.

The difficulty with the percentage-of-completion method is in estimating the progress achieved. If the estimate is optimistic, income will be over-stated in the current period and understated in future periods. Conversely, if the evaluation of progress is pessimistic, income for the current period will be understated and future periods will be overstated.

We shall not attempt to state which method of accounting should be followed, because the business objectives and composition of management in each architectural and engineering firm are different and individual requirements may vary. The firm's records might be maintained on a completed-contract or cash basis for determining income or loss for tax purposes or reporting to creditors. At the same time, percentage-of-completion records may be maintained on a "memo basis" in order to relate income and expense to the specific periods of operations. The percentage-of-completion method will almost always provide the professional architect or engineer with better information to control and manage his business more effectively. It is the management information and control aspect of accounting to which we shall direct our attention in this chapter.

6.3   What Is Management Information and Control in an Architectural or Engineering Firm?

The term "management" has been defined as "the act or art of managing; control, direction;" "information" has been defined as "the communication or reception of knowledge or intelligence."[2] Therein lies the basic definition of a management information and control system. A management information and control system involves the elements of organizing, planning, executing, controlling, and communicating knowledge. In order to do good professional work, an architectural or engineering firm requires good organization, direction, and information.

Such a system should be directed primarily at the principal control elements in the business and how these elements relate to the firm's organization and profit plans. The principal control elements in architectural and engineering firms are (1) the time of the professional personnel, (2) the pricing of professional time, (3) unbilled costs, (4) billed costs, and (5) overhead.

6.4   Professional Time

Architects and engineers sell a service which is comprised of the collective time and talent of their professional personnel. Adequate control over the utilization of personnel is essential to profitable operations. To the extent that professional personnel spend their time on productive work, such time is considered to be "chargeable" to the client and is a potential source of revenue. If their time is "nonchargeable" to a client, it becomes an overhead cost to the firm.

For a system to produce meaningful and useful information, timely and accurate source reporting is required; and source reporting in this case is personnel time. Each individual in the firm must maintain adequate time records and, at periodic intervals, report his time showing chargeable time by individual clients and/or jobs and nonchargeable time by the appropriate overhead expense classification. Chargeable time should be reported by project so that the proper job is charged for the time. Nonchargeable time should be reported as to vacation, illness, promotion, civic responsibilities, etc., so that these overhead items can be adequately controlled. Information can then be provided by the system, summarizing the ratio of chargeable hours by individuals as well as departments.

6.5 Pricing of Professional Time

The revenues generated by the architect or engineering firm are derived from the services of their professional personnel. These services can be translated into time, and there are a number of ways in which the time of these professionals can be billed to a client. It is from the revenues produced by the professional personnel that their salaries are paid, overhead and administrative costs are met, and income is derived for the principals of the firm.

It is essential that the pricing of professional time be fair to all concerned. It must be fair to the client in relation to the service rendered; it must be fair to the employees in terms of salaries commensurate with their talents; and it must be fair to the principals in terms of adequate return on their investment and compensation for their individual effort and assumption of entrepreneurial risks.

Several methods are used by architects and engineers to price their services. One common pricing method is to bill salary plus a specific percentage (such as 150 percent, which is equivalent to two and one-half times time card labor costs) to cover overhead and profit. Another common method is to establish a per diem rate which includes salary, overhead, and profit factors. Our discussion and illustrations will assume the use of the per diem rate concept for pricing professional time.

The use of a per diem rate structure is relatively easy to administer and facilitates the establishment of profit plans. Personnel are categorized and a standard per diem rate is established for each category which gives consideration to overhead and profit and to the expected chargeable ratio discussed above. Revenue budgets or plans can then be derived by extending the ratio by category by the expected chargeable hours.

The per diem rate structure also provides a sound basis for controlling performance in relation to profit plans. If profits are not adequate, several courses of action are open to management:

1. The hourly per diem rates could be increased. However, this alternative may not be fair to the client in relation to competing firms.

2. The chargeable ratio could be increased.

3. Overhead could be reduced. An increase in chargeable time may also bring about a decrease in the relative amount of overhead.

6.6   Unbilled and Billed Costs

Even though a firm maintains excellent control over the utilization of its professional time, it is not assured of obtaining adequate profits. During the course of a project the costs incurred are charged to unbilled costs. And, in the final analysis, when the job is closed, the true value of the unbilled costs and profits obtained for the principals is determined only when they have been billed to and collected from the respective clients.

One of the key factors involved in controlling unbilled and billed costs is the basic relationship established with the client. It is essential that a clear understanding be formulated at the outset of an engagement regarding the amount of fees and method of computation, the reimbursement of out-of-pocket expenses, and arrangements regarding the frequency of billing.

The use of a per diem rate structure provides still another basis for controlling unbilled and billed costs. Since the per diem value contains salary, overhead, and profit, the total per diem value of unbilled time costs for a project is the amount that should be billed to a client. This will not always be the amount billable to the client, but any adjustments can be readily identified and responsibility therefore fixed. Basically there are two reasons why the billing might differ from the per diem value of unbilled time:

1. The fee arrangement varies from the fee structure, and responsibility for such unbillable amounts lies with the principal of the firm accepting the work.

2. Some of the time expended to do the work is simply not billable time. This could indicate the inefficient use of professional personnel for which responsibility rests with the supervisory personnel in the area or areas concerned.

Cash flow is another key factor involved in controlling unbilled and billed costs. Cash must be generated to meet payroll and other day-to-day expenses of the business. In order to meet these cash requirements, costs and profits accumulated by the project must be billed and collected from the clients or the firm may have to borrow operating funds. And, of course, borrowing introduces additional overhead cost—interest charges—to the business.

One relatively simple approach to help management control unbilled and billed costs and expenses is to establish a standard against which the investment in these costs will be measured. If an adequate annual revenue budget has been developed, the daily cash requirement can be derived by dividing the total by the number of days in a year. The investment in billed and unbilled costs can then be divided by the daily cash requirement to determine the number of days "invested" in these items. Management can relate the number of days of investment in these items to their operating plan to determine any action required.

6.7   Overhead

Another key control element in the architect or engineer's office is overhead. It is also the part of the business which often gets too little attention. There are many ways to report overhead expenses; but to facilitate control, the information should be directed to those responsible for the costs who should also have authority to take whatever corrective action may be necessary. Overhead may be thought of in terms of (1) fixed expenses, (2) labor expenses, (3) controllable expenses.

Fixed expenses are those items over which little control can be exercised on a short-term basis, especially when a firm's activity level is fluctuating. These expenses include such things as rent, utilities, insurance, and depreciation of furniture and equipment. Fixed expenses should be charged to the person in charge of administration whose responsibility it is to maintain reasonable balance between these costs and the firm's activity level.

Labor expenses are directly related to the personnel employed by the firm and contain some of the characteristics of fixed as well as controllable expenses. This would include the salaries of all administrative personnel such as accounting clerks and secretaries, and it would also include such items as vacations, illness, payroll taxes, and other employee benefits for professional personnel. Control information for these expenses would normally be reported by area of responsibility and would compare actual expenses with the predetermined plan or budget.

Similarly, controllable expenses would relate actual expenses to the budget on a responsibility basis. Responsibility for controllable overhead costs is normally assigned to the person in charge of administration. Controllable expenses include such items as charitable contributions, professional society dues, subscriptions, supplies, and outside services.

ILLUSTRATIONS OF MANAGEMENT INFORMATION

6.8 Organization

We have discussed the general concepts of management information for control in an architectural or engineering firm. Now let us examine these concepts in an assumed situation. It should be noted that the emphasis has been placed on reporting information to the individual being held responsible for the activity or function and who has authority to take necessary corrective action. The architectural partnership of Martin and Becker, which operates entirely out of one office, will be used to illustrate an information-reporting system.

The Martin and Becker partnership is a happy blend in that Mr. Martin is business-oriented and well suited to perform the administrative duties of the firm as well as oversee project management while Mr. Becker, on the other hand, is more oriented toward the design and technical aspects of the firm's operations. For these reasons the two partners have organized their firm and established responsibilities along the lines indicated in Fig. 6.1.

The project managers are responsible for the overall coordination of the job through its various stages, meeting with and satisfying client requests, and billing and collecting the fees. Simply stated, they are responsible for the management of each of their engagements to a profitable conclusion.

The departmental heads must determine that the work performed coincides with the project's objectives, that the work meets the standards established by the firm, and that the task is accomplished in an efficient and timely manner.

The budgets for each job are established through the cooperation of the various department heads and the project manager. Each is then responsible to see that his portion of the work is performed in accordance with his plan. If the budgeted fee does not coincide with the aggregate labor, direct job costs, and profit target, the project has simply been sold or accepted on another basis. The difference between actual fee to be earned and planned fee is ordinarily the responsibility of the partners, because only they have authority to establish a price for which the firm will work.

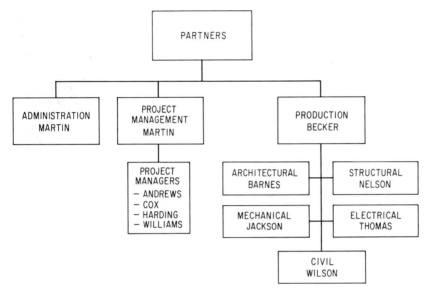

Fig. 6.1   Martin and Becker partnership

6.9   Control of Professional Time

If the heads of the architectural, structural, mechanical, electrical, and civil departments are responsible for performing their portion of a project in accordance with planned expenditures, two requirements are necessary:

1. A cardinal principle of responsibility reporting for control is that the person held responsible must at least agree to the budget established, and preferably he should participate in its preparation.

2. Information relating performance in an individual's area of responsibility must be reported on a timely basis so that appropriate action may be exercised. The key here is information for control, and if the data are not timely, the department head will have difficulty in maintaining control.

A "project labor report" is prepared for each department head. Figure 6.2 illustrates pertinent information shown for the Winston Park School project for Mr. Barnes of the architectural department. Similar information is shown for each project and a total for the department is also prepared. The report indicates the personnel who have charged time to the project during the current period as well as the total per diem for the period. Mr. Barnes knows who he has assigned to the various projects, and this provides him the ability to see that their time is being charged to the proper jobs.

The project-to-date information is the key to how the department has performed by project and in total for all jobs. The department considers

PROJECT LABOR REPORT			ARCHITECTURAL			PERIOD ENDED 4-30-67				
						‑ ‑ ‑ ‑ ‑ PROJECT TO DATE ‑ ‑ ‑ ‑ ‑ ‑				OVER(-)
PROJECT NO.	PROJECT TITLE OR NAME		EMPL. CLASS.	– CURRENT PERIOD – HOURS PER DIEM		PLANNED	%	‑ ‑ ‑ COMPLETED ‑ ‑ ‑ PLAN	ACTUAL	UNDER PLAN
4206	WINSTON PARK SCHOOL									
		CARLSON	A-SR	8	$ 224				$ 1,400	
		DENZ	A	12	264				1,320	
		LEWIS	A-JR	10	180				1,800	
TOTAL PROJECT					$ 668	$ 9,000	45	$ 4,050	$ 4,520	$ 470-
TOTAL ARCHITECTURAL					$ 73,779			$ 222,664	$230,606	$ 7,942-

Fig. 6.2   Project labor report

itself to be 45 percent complete on the Winston Park School project. Based on this estimate of percent of completion, the department has spent $470 in excess of its plan. This could mean that they were inefficient, that they have underestimated their percent of completion, or that the estimated cost of the work to be done was too low. It is Mr. Barnes's responsibility then to analyze each job as to the estimate for its completion or efficiency because the department has exceeded its planned expenditures by $7,942.

In addition to his responsibility for performing work on projects in accordance with planned expenditures, Mr. Barnes is also accountable for controlling the nonchargeable time or overhead of his professional staff. He receives a detail labor report (Fig. 6.3) indicating how each employee in the department has spent his time for the current period. In addition, the ratio of time chargeable to projects is shown for both the current period and the year to date. A similar report is prepared for each department in the firm.

The detail labor report indicates that the architectural department has a 78 percent chargeable ratio for the current year and 83 percent for the current period. Assuming the planned chargeable ratio is 85 percent, overhead costs are somewhat higher than anticipated. Couple this information with the fact that the department is almost $8,000 over planned expenses on projects in process, and it is obvious that Mr. Barnes has a problem. He is probably overstaffed for the present activity load.

The final responsibility for the overall performance of the firm rests with the partners, and as indicated in Fig. 6.1, Mr. Becker manages the production departments. It is not necessary for him to receive all the detail information by project or employee provided the department heads, but he

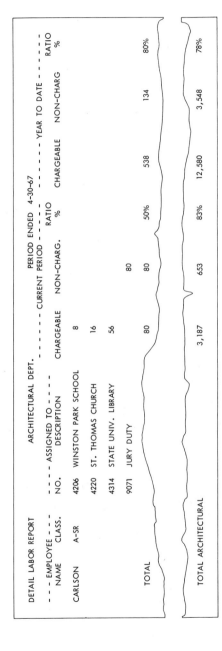

DETAIL LABOR REPORT   ARCHITECTURAL DEPT.   PERIOD ENDED 4-30-67

| EMPLOYEE | | ASSIGNED TO | | CURRENT PERIOD | | | YEAR TO DATE | | |
NAME	CLASS.	NO.	DESCRIPTION	CHARGEABLE	NON-CHARG.	RATIO %	CHARGEABLE	NON-CHARG	RATIO %
CARLSON	A-SR	4206	WINSTON PARK SCHOOL	8					
		4220	ST. THOMAS CHURCH	16					
		4314	STATE UNIV. LIBRARY	56					
		9071	JURY DUTY		80				
TOTAL				80	80	50%	538	134	80%
TOTAL ARCHITECTURAL				3,187	653	83%	12,580	3,548	78%

Fig. 6.3 Detail labor report by department (in hours)

DEPARTMENT	PRODUCTION EFFICIENCY REPORT						PERIOD ENDED 4-30-67		
	- - - - - CURRENT PERIOD - - - - -			- - - - - - YEAR TO DATE - - - - -			- - PROJECTS TO DATE - - -		OVER(-) UNDER PLAN
	CHARGEABLE HOURS	NON-CHARG. HOURS	RATIO	CHARGEABLE HOURS	NON-CHARG. HOURS	RATIO %	PLAN	ACTUAL	
ARCHITECTURAL	3,187	653	83%	12,580	3,548	78%	$ 222,664	$ 230,606	$ 7,942-
STRUCTURAL	1,203	77	94	5,161	215	96	66,799	72,267	5,468-
MECHANICAL	1,346	254	86	6,182	538	92	89,066	88,635	431
ELECTRICAL	1,253	187	87	5,504	544	91	77,932	82,054	4,122-
CIVIL	437	43	91	1,914	102	95	22,266	21,430	836
TOTAL	7,426	1,214	86%	31,341	4,947	86%	$ 478,727	$ 494,992	$ 16,265-

Fig. 6.4   Production efficiency report

should obtain the summary information illustrated in the production efficiency report (Fig. 6.4) to discharge his responsibility.

The "production efficiency report" serves two purposes for Mr. Becker. First, he can observe the chargeable ratio for the most recent accounting period, as well as for the year to date. And, secondly, he can observe how well each department is performing its work on the projects in process. The departments are expected to complete each project within their planned expenditures, and the architectural department is expected to maintain an 85 percent chargeable ratio while all other departments are budgeted to be 92 percent chargeable.

Mr. Becker knows that a problem has developed in the architectural department. For the year to date, the department is 7 percent below its expected chargeable ratio, which will have an adverse effect on overhead costs. This large deviation from the planned level of activity amounts to almost two people. At the same time, the department has expended nearly $8,000 in excess of its estimates for jobs in progress. When this situation is reviewed with Mr. Barnes, head of the architectural department, Mr. Becker will probably look for the reduction of at least one and perhaps two people from the professional staff.

The structural department has been maintaining a chargeable ratio higher than expected. However, Mr. Becker will want to know why expenses on the projects in process are considerably greater than planned. To the extent that the excess per diems are not billable to clients, the personnel costs will reduce net income to the partnership in the same way as excessive nonchargeable time.

Even though the chargeable ratio of the mechanical department is below expected levels for the current accounting period, the year-to-date ratio as well as performance on projects in process is on target and does not appear to be posing any problem for the firm. The civil department is also performing satisfactorily.

Mr. Becker will probably want to review the situation in the electrical department. Per diems for work in process are significantly in excess of planned charges. In addition, the chargeable ratio is below expectations. It may not be significant that the chargeable ratio is only 1 percent below plan for the year to date, but it is important to note that the department fell 5 percent below expectations in the current period, and this occurred at the same time that charges to projects are exceeding budget.

6.10   Project Control

In addition to maintaining control over professional time, it is also essential to exercise proper control over each project. A manager is assigned to each project to coordinate all activities on the job. He coordinates the preparation of the budget for each job. He may assist the partner in negotiating the fee. He coordinates the work in the various departments with client requirements, and he may do the billing and collect the fees from the client.

The project report gives a complete picture of a particular job at the conclusion of an accounting period. If the report is to be useful to the project manager, it must be prepared shortly after the end of the accounting period. Only through timely information can corrective action be initiated to remedy a problem or ward off a potential difficulty.

Figure 6.5 is the project report for Mr. Andrews on the Winston Park

PROJECT REPORT FOR ANDREWS - JOB 4206   WINSTON PARK SCHOOL   PERIOD ENDED 4-30-67

DESCRIPTION			- - - - PROJECT TO DATE - - - - -		
			- COMPLETED -		OVER(-) UNDER
	PLANNED	%	PLANNED	ACTUAL	PLAN
LABOR					
PARTNER LABOR	1,125	50	563	600	37-
PROJECT MANAGEMENT	2,025	30	608	570	38
ARCHITECTURAL	9,000	45	4,050	4,520	470-
STRUCTURAL	2,700	30	810	850	40-
MECHANICAL	3,600	25	900	935	35-
ELECTRICAL	3,150	25	788	720	68
CIVIL	900	60	540	510	30
TOTAL PER DIEM	22,500		8,259	8,705	446-
DIRECT COSTS	500	15	75	93	18-
TOTAL PROJECT FEE PLANNED	23,000	36	8,334	8,798	464-
ACTUAL FEE TO BE EARNED AND BILLED	22,000	36		7,920	
PLANNED FEE OVER(-) UNDER CONTRACT FEE	1,000-				
AMOUNT BILLED TO DATE				5,500	
UNBILLED FEES EARNED				2,420	
UNCOLLECTED FEES BILLED				3,000	

Fig. 6.5   Project report

School job. The per diems estimated to complete the project plus direct job costs total $23,000. However, the partners have accepted the job for a fixed fee of $22,000. The partners bear the responsibility for the loss of $1,000 in fees, and the resulting reduction of profit on the job, of course, is their prerogative.

It is important to emphasize that the per diem estimates should be made prior to negotiating a fixed fee. In this instance we assume that the partners accepted the work for a reduced fee from a knowledgeable position. If a job is not evaluated and fees estimated in advance of negotiations, it can be very costly to a firm, especially when a client wants a fixed- or maximum-fee arrangement.

Mr. Andrews is not responsible for the sacrifice of $1,000 in fees, but he is jointly responsible to complete the work for $23,000. He knows that the architectural department is basically responsible for the excess costs to date. He will review this with Mr. Barnes to determine the cause. The estimate of completion might be too low, and he will want to review that situation carefully.

In addition, he will review all the percentage-of-completion estimates to evaluate the accuracy of such reporting, because it is used as the criterion for billing. Based on the aggregate completion stage of all departments ($8,334), the overall percentage of completion is computed to be 36 percent. Therefore, 36 percent of the planned fee for the Winston Park School has been earned.

The actual fee of $22,000 will be the total billing for the project. Mr. Andrews can now bill 36 percent, or $7,920, because that much of the work has been completed and earned. The project report further informs him that he has previously billed $5,500; therefore, he has $2,420 in unbilled costs to be billed at this time. And the report further informs him that, of the amounts previously billed, $3,000 still remains to be collected.

So that Mr. Martin can meet his responsibilities to the partnership, he receives a fee summary report (Fig. 6.6) at the conclusion of each accounting period. The information is summarized by project managers because, as in the production departments, any action that Mr. Martin may direct will be on a responsibility basis.

The pricing information, while reported by project manager because it is summarized from the individual jobs, is the responsibility of the partners of the firm. It is good, nonetheless, to report this information so that they are constantly apprised of the total effect of deviations from the per diem structure.

The efficiency relates the overall performance on all jobs presently in process. It is reported by project managers because they are responsible for coordinating all activities and seeing them to a successful conclusion. In this case, two project managers, Andrews and Harding, are experiencing large variations from their planned expenditures. Mr. Martin will surely want to review the situation with these two men, especially Mr. Harding.

It will be noted that actual efficiency is adverse and exceeds plan by $18,920. It was reported to Mr. Becker on the production efficiency report (Fig. 6.4) that the production departments exceeded their plans by $16,265. The other $2,655 variance is in the partner or project-manager time and direct job costs which are reported to the project manager on the project report.

The actual fee earned is the aggregate percent of completion for the firm, wherein the Winston Park School project is 36 percent complete and has earned $7,920 (Fig. 6.5), and the total of all jobs in process is a little over 50 percent complete at the end of the April 30, 1967, accounting period. Mr. Martin will probably be concerned about the fact that all the work in the office represents less than one-half year in revenues (177 days) and they are a little over one-half complete (92 days) on those jobs.

The investment in billed and unbilled costs is also summarized by the project manager so that Mr. Martin can evaluate how well they are billing the fees earned and collecting the fees billed. In addition, the total investment in billed and unbilled costs in terms of number of days' revenue is 82. Since the partners' plan is to hold their investment within a 90-day limit, there does not appear to be any major overall problem in billing and collecting their fees at this time. However, he will undoubtedly conduct a review with his project managers to determine that there are no specific client problems which have a significant effect on the overall picture.

FEE SUMMARY REPORT						PERIOD ENDED 4-30-67			
	- - - - - PRICING - - - - -			- - - - EFFICIENCY - - - -				- - - - INVESTMENT - - - -	
PROJECT MANAGER	PLAN	ACTUAL	OVER UNDER(-) PLAN	PLAN	ACTUAL	OVER(-) UNDER PLAN	ACTUAL FEE EARNED	UNBILLED COSTS	BILLED COSTS
ANDREWS	256,000	260,000	4,000	77,800	81,640	3,840-	78,000	54,600	15,600
COX	295,000	284,000	11,000-	162,250	161,325	925	156,200	82,226	54,670
HARDING	273,000	269,000	4,000-	131,040	147,215	16,175-	129,120	52,940	38,736
WILLIAMS	241,000	247,000	6,000	185,570	185,400	170	190,190	114,114	76,076
TOTAL	1,065,000	1,060,000	5,000-	556,660	575,580	18,920-	553,510	303,880	185,082
NUMBER OF DAYS	177						92	51	31

Fig. 6.6   Fee summary report (in dollars)

6.11   Overhead Control

In addition to project administration, Mr. Martin also conducts the overall administration of the firm. In connection with this duty he receives a labor overhead report (Fig. 6.7) which summarizes information by areas of responsibility. Included would be the cost for nonchargeable professional time, cost of administrative personnel, payroll taxes, vacations, etc. There is more detail reporting for these overhead items on a departmental basis in support of this summary report, but we shall confine our discussion to the information Mr. Martin receives.

The labor overhead report relates the fact that the firm has expended more than $10,000 in excess of their plans for the year to date. Basically, the architectural department accounts for the entire excess. Mr. Martin will note, however, that the mechanical department had a serious deviation from planned expenses in the current period. Furthermore, he will recognize from the fee summary report (Fig. 6.6) that the total fees to be earned for all jobs in process are just over one million; and at the present staff level, this represents 177 days or about one-half year's activity. To maintain the present staff level, the firm requires about $2.2 million a year in fees.

Based on this information, it would appear that the partners have a serious problem confronting them. They need considerably more business to support the organization they now employ, as evidenced by the fact that they have begun to experience an undesirable amount of nonchargeable time from the professional group. Either new business or a reduction in personnel is required to maintain an adequate profit for the firm.

LABOR OVERHEAD REPORT				PERIOD ENDED 4-30-67		
	- - - CURRENT PERIOD - - - - - -			- - - - YEAR TO DATE - - - -		
DESCRIPTION	PLANNED	ACTUAL	OVER(-) UNDER PLAN	PLANNED	ACTUAL	OVER(-) UNDER PLAN
PROJECT MANAGEMENT	2,077	2,129	52-	8,707	10,306	1,599-
ARCHITECTURAL	9,598	10,210	612-	40,325	50,753	10,428-
STRUCTURAL	2,046	1,844	202	8,600	6,881	1,719
MECHANICAL	1,650	3,650	2,000-	11,012	10,992	20-
ELECTRICAL	2,356	2,933	577-	9,904	10,461	577-
CIVIL	765	819	54-	3,223	2,716	507
ADMINISTRATIVE	4,480	4,500	20-	18,816	18,800	16
	22,972	26,085	3,113-	100,587	110,909	10,322-

Fig. 6.7   Labor overhead report

GENERAL OVERHEAD REPORT				PERIOD ENDED 4-30-67		
	- - - CURRENT PERIOD - - -			- - - - YEAR TO DATE - - - -		
DESCRIPTION	PLANNED	ACTUAL	OVER(-) UNDER PLAN	PLANNED	ACTUAL	OVER(-) UNDER PLAN
CONTROLLABLE EXPENSES						
SUPPLIES	2,200	1,644	556	8,750	8,856	106-
TELEPHONE AND TELEGRAPH	830	617	213	3,300	3,321	21-
SERVICES	1,950	1,541	409	8,500	8,303	197
CONTRIBUTIONS	275	206	69	1,100	1,107	7-
GENERAL EXPENSES	4,200	3,083	1,117	16,000	16,605	605-
TOTAL CONTROLLABLE EXPENSES	9,455	7,091	2,364	37,650	38,192	542-
FIXED EXPENSES						
RENT AND UTILITIES	5,900	5,847	53	23,500	23,800	300-
INSURANCE	970	925	45	3,900	3,875	25
DEPRECIATION	844	844	-	3,380	3,375	5
TOTAL FIXED EXPENSES	7,714	7,616	98	30,780	31,050	270-
TOTAL GENERAL OVERHEAD	17,169	14,707	2,462	68,430	69,242	812-

Fig. 6.8   General overhead report

In addition to labor overhead, a report of all other overhead is prepared for the administrative head of the firm. Normally, such a report would differentiate between controllable and fixed expenses as illustrated in the general overhead report (Fig. 6.8). Like the other reports we have discussed, information such as this provides the partners an opportunity to review what has taken place in relation to their plans and quickly spot any problem areas that require attention. In this case, Mr. Martin will observe that overhead expenses are being incurred about as expected.

6.12   Comments on Computerizing Management Information Systems

The above discussion is not intended to imply that these are the only reports required by the Martin and Becker partnership. Neither is it intended to imply that these reports should be the operating information presented in every instance. The concept of the reporting system should reflect the organization and personality of the firm.

If the firm is managed by a single principal, the information we have discussed might be inappropriate. The principal in such a case is the management information system in that he "lives" with each job every day. However, it would still be appropriate to accumulate costs by jobs for reference when estimating jobs of a similar nature in the future.

Management information such as we have discussed becomes applicable when two or more principles are involved and responsibilities for the various firm activities are divided. The techniques or methods of preparing such information are many and varied, and may range from a completely manual to a completely computerized system.

In a small firm it is usually more economical to produce the information reports on a manual basis. This is generally true because the small firm does not have the volume of transactions to require mechanized equipment; and because the firm is small, it frequently does not require a great deal of reporting. It should be pointed out, however, that many small firms do have computers to satisfy their computational needs in other areas. In this case, computerization of even a small firm's records may be economically justifiable.

When a firm reaches a certain size, it becomes economical to mechanize the payroll, project, and efficiency reporting systems such as we have discussed. It is impossible to state when or at what specific size it becomes economical for a firm to mechanize. The reporting should reflect management's needs, which can and frequently do vary significantly between firms of equal size.

For example, the project report (Fig. 6.5) which we discussed is satisfactory for the Martin and Becker firm. Another firm may want to report actual versus planned for the current accounting period and fiscal year to date as well as on the project-to-date basis. This would provide the ability to summarize the monthly and year-to-date figures into a monthly income and loss statement which they need.

One of the ways to mechanize a management information system is to use a service center. A number of different kinds of such service centers are in operation. There are large national firms that perform data-processing services for local concerns as well as enterprises with many facilities. There are smaller local firms performing the same service of processing customer data on their computers. In addition, many banks are utilizing their unused computer time to perform services for their customers.

The services rendered by these firms vary in accordance with the requirements of their customer. For instance, a service center will assist in the design and programming of the system to their computer as well as process the data on a regular basis. In addition to the regular processing charges, there is a fee or one-time charge to design and program the system. Banks, for instance, vary their charges based upon the magnitude of the deposit a customer maintains in the bank.

A firm can design and program its own system, which will then be processed on a service center's computer. This, of course, requires employment of personnel to do this type of work not only for the initial conversion but also to maintain the system.

Another alternative is for a firm to acquire its own computer on a rental or purchase basis to perform the data-processing activities. In addition to the systems and programming personnel mentioned above, the alternative also requires personnel to operate the equipment. Systems, programming, and computer operating can be overlapping functions; the amount of overlap is dependent on the magnitude of the problem.

It is also possible for data-processing or accounting personnel to share a computer with the technical or professional personnel of the firm. For a small professional office, this is a very common way of operating. It might be pointed out, however, that there may be some differences in the precise computer specification requirements which have to be coordinated when merging these activities because of the basic difference in the input-output requirements of data processing and architectural-engineering work.

Another means of access to computing power is to have an input-output terminal in the professional office which receives and transmits data to a time-sharing computer complex. Many architectural and engineering firms as well as many other businesses are performing statistical and other analytical problems in this manner. Undoubtedly, it will soon be feasible to mechanize payrolls and management information systems such as we have discussed in a similar manner.

6.13   Accounting and the Critical-path Method

The use of the critical-path method for office scheduling and manpower requirements is discussed in detail in Chapter 7. However, it should be obvious that the critical-path method is also pertinent to a management information reporting system such as we have discussed.

In the illustrations of management information, actual results were often compared with planned results. Therefore, a detailed analysis had to be made of each aspect of a job at the outset. The time required to perform each task had to be estimated and translated into a dollar value. Critical path is merely another manner in which to plan and estimate time by the activities required to accomplish a task.

It would follow, then, that if a firm is going to utilize the critical-path method for scheduling professional personnel, the coding structure should be such that an individual's time reporting can serve both accounting and scheduling operations. In addition, information reporting by jobs could relate actual versus planned by the activities on the critical-path schedule. For example, the project labor report (Fig. 6.2) could report the Winston Park School project by the critical-path activity code for the architectural department.

The reporting of information which incorporates the critical-path approach will be more detailed than that required by most accounting methods. However, a firm that finds it beneficial to use critical-path scheduling should also be able to reap the benefits of the by-product financial information readily available. It seems almost certain that the eventual integration of office scheduling techniques with accounting and management information systems will produce an extremely powerful tool for control of project costs and schedules.

6.14 Conclusion

In conclusion it may be said that, in modern business, the accounting function has evolved into a controllership function. This is accomplished by planning what is expected to be accomplished and reporting actual results on a timely basis so that necessary management evaluation and control may be made at the appropriate responsibility levels in the organization.

Furthermore, the accounting function has a unique modern tool at its disposal to discharge its controllership function—the computer. The computer provides the capacity to develop meaningful information reports on a basis more timely than ever before. Architects and engineers are discovering that the development of a management information reporting concept utilizing computer technology is as useful to them as it is to other business concerns.

REFERENCES

1. H. A. Finney and H. E. Miller, *Principles of Accounting—Intermediate*, 4th ed., p. 19, Prentice-Hall, Inc., Englewood Cliffs, N.J., January, 1956.
2. *Webster's Seventh New Collegiate Dictionary*, G. & C. Merriam Company, Springfield, Mass., 1965.

CHAPTER SEVEN

Computer-based Management Techniques for the Architectural- Engineering Office

By William H. Linder

This chapter treats the general problem of network scheduling, in the context of scheduling work within the individual architectural-engineering office. The key developments of CPM and PERT are placed in historical perspective. A brief presentation of a new problem-oriented language (PROJECT) for facilitating the use of general network techniques is given in the concluding sections of the chapter.

*Dr. Linder is an Assistant Professor in the
Department of Computer Science at the
University of South Carolina. He was graduated
from the U.S. Military Academy, West Point,
with a B.S. degree in 1956. After serving with
the Corps of Engineers, he came to study at
M.I.T., where he was awarded an M.S. degree in
Civil Engineering in 1965 and a Ph. D. degree
in Civil Engineering Systems in 1968. While at
M.I.T., Dr. Linder was on the staff of the
Department of Civil Engineering, where he
worked as a research assistant and an instructor,
teaching a course in project management and
developing the problem-oriented computer
language PROJECT.*

7.1 Introduction

The high-speed digital computer is a flexible tool which can be used by the professional architect-engineer in a number of helpful ways. In recent years a great many computer-based management procedures have been developed to assist the engineer-manager in planning, scheduling, and controlling the work done in accomplishing large engineering projects. These same techniques and procedures can be used effectively in managing the flow of work through the office of the professional architect-engineer.

The usefulness of these project-management techniques has already been recognized by a number of architectural-engineering offices, judging from the inquiries coming from interested offices, the number of architectural students taking engineering courses in project management, and the offices now using the project network for planning their work. A group of architects, engineers, and graduate students, working at M.I.T. under Prof. Albert G. Dietz in the Center for Building Research, has made good use of the project network in its research projects. Several articles have appeared in professional magazines telling how the project network is used in leading offices across the country.

In the *Inland Architect* of January, 1967, an article by Thomas J. Eyerman tells how the Chicago office of Skidmore, Owings and Merrill has come to use the project network for planning, scheduling, and monitoring their office work. Then in the February and March, 1967, issues of *Architectural Record* a two-part article tells about the project network and how it is used successfully in the office of Golemon and Rolfe of Houston, Texas.

There is a wide range of project-management techniques and procedures, and using the network is only a beginning. Making up a project network is an investment in time from which much can be gained in addition to the first step of calculating a schedule. The purpose of this chapter is to give a brief overview of project management and show *where* the techniques and procedures can be used, *what* they will do for office management, and *how* one system of computer programs might be used in an architectural-engineering office. This chapter can be an introduction to project-management technology for those firms which are interested but have not yet begun to use project-management techniques, and it can present a broader view of project management to the firms which might already be using some of the techniques.

The contents of the chapter fall naturally into three major areas of concentration: (1) the computer in project management, (2) project-management technology, and (3) a demonstration of how the flow of work in an architectural-engineering office can be handled in terms of multi-project management. Sections 7.2 and 7.3 describe the use of the computer for project planning and control, the advantages and justification. Sections 7.4 through 7.9 tell of the project as a representation of work and relate this to the flow of work through an architectural-engineering office. These sections also contain a discussion of some of the project-management techniques and a description of how they may be used in the office to control the flow of work. Sections 7.10, 7.11 and 7.12 demonstrate one particular system of project-management techniques which is structured as a problem-oriented language. Included there is an example of how this language, PROJECT, might be used in a professional office.

7.2 The Role of the Computer

The quantitative techniques and procedures used for project management are mostly straightforward and rather easily understood. The basic procedure is network scheduling, which generates a project schedule and serves as a basis for a great many other operations, such as estimating, cost control, and allocation of office manpower.

Network scheduling is essentially a simple procedure, and the best way to learn to use it and to appreciate its simplicity is to set up a small-scale network and work out the calculations with pencil and paper. While the calculations themselves, additions, subtractions, and comparisons, are simple enough, the complexity increases significantly as a larger network is used to represent a full-scale problem, and as details are added to the network to support other project-management procedures. With even a moderately sized network, keeping track of this detailed information and making a great number of simple calculations becomes very tedious and burdensome. One answer to this problem of tedious and repetitive calculation and data handling is the computational capacity of modern digital computers.

One of the most powerful capabilities of the computer is its almost unbelievable speed in making simple, accurate calculations and comparisons. When a large quantity of calculations are to be made, it is frequently more economical to have them done by computer than by an engineer or clerk. As the number of calculations goes up, the economic advantage of the computer increases rapidly.

A decision that project-management calculations are to be made by hand drastically limits the benefits of using the project-management techniques described in this chapter. Such a decision almost necessarily implies that other techniques, including those handling manpower scheduling and cash flow, will not be used and that the network schedule will not be updated and recalculated as often as might be necessary. Changes in the work plan or adjustment of the schedule on the basis of actual progress usually require modification of the network and recalculation of the schedule. If the network and schedule are not kept up to date by making these modifications and recalculations, both network and schedule will rapidly lose their value. On the basis of the many benefits to be gained by effectively using project-management techniques, the number of calculations to be made, and the amount of detailed information to be kept in order, the architectural-engineering office wanting to get full value out of time and effort spent on project-management techniques may be very well advised to consider using computer-based project-management techniques.

7.3   A Note on Computer Programs for Project Management

An interesting perspective on computer programs for project management is offered by the following analogy, where a computer and computer program are compared with a player piano and the perforated piano roll that causes a player piano to play a particular tune. Just as a player piano can play any of a variety of tunes according to the piano rolls on hand, a computer can perform any of a variety of tasks according to the particular programs available. Similarly, just as there might be many different piano-roll versions of one tune and some of these versions might be more pleasing than others, so a variety of computer programs are available for performing a particular operation, and some programs give a more suitable performance than others.

When an office decides to use computer-based project-management techniques, arrangements must be made to get access to both a computer and the proper computer programs. A selection of project-management programs is normally available through the manufacturer for most computers currently on the market. The first step in choosing some of these programs might be to make a survey of the project-management programs available and to select from these the programs best suited to the needs of the office. A good basis for comparing programs can be found in Chapter 10 and Appendix 10.1 of Reference 2, where there is a fairly complete listing of various programs and their features. Programs which have become available since this book was published in 1964 should be added to the list and compared on the same basis.

Despite the existence of some excellent project-management programs, nearly all have inherent limitations which have been typical of historical computer usage. First, a computer program, once written, is restricted to performing the same task in the same way under the same set of conditions. Second, each computer program has its own rigid format for data to be used with that program. The project data must be put into exactly this format by someone familiar with the program being used. Third, after an office has selected a set of programs and has become accustomed to using them, it is difficult to modify either the programs or office practice hinging upon those programs. This lack of flexibility in computer programs has put severe limitations on the use of the computer in the engineering office.

To overcome some of these limitations, the Civil Engineering Systems Laboratory of the Department of Civil Engineering at M.I.T. has conducted a large-scale research program[4] over several years. This research program has met with much success, chiefly by developing the problem-oriented-language concept, which provides a new and more flexible communication link between man and machine.

7.4   The Office Job as a Project

The project-management techniques used today have been developed primarily for use in the area of building construction, planning and construction of industrial facilities, and management of large-scale research and development programs, usually those sponsored by the National Aeronautic and Space Administration or the U.S. Department of Defense. Although these areas differ a great deal in the type of work done and in the product turned out, they are very much alike in a way quite important for management. Work in each of these three areas is organized formally as a project so that computer-based project planning and control techniques can be used in its management. These same project-management techniques can be used very effectively in the architectural-engineering office when the jobs coming into the office are treated as projects.

A project can be thought of as the accomplishment of any task which satisfies three rather simple conditions. The three conditions necessary for a task to be handled as a project are (1) that its end product is specified, (2) that its accomplishment requires the use of some scarce or expensive resources, and (3) that the work necessary can be listed in terms of separate work items or subtasks. A task meeting these three conditions takes the form of a project when the work planned to produce the specified end product has been divided into separate subtasks and thus a work plan has been made up. The working out of this work plan is the implementation of the project.

The jobs done in an architectural-engineering office almost always satisfy these three conditions and can therefore be thought of as projects. The office work has a specified end product—usually a series of drawings and specifications. This work must be accomplished using expensive resources —the time of the office personnel who must design, draft, and write specifications. And the accomplishment of the office work is laid out as a number of subtasks, if not formally as a written work plan, then at least informally in the head of the responsible supervisor. While the work done in the architectural-engineering office might be thought of by the client as just one phase of a larger job, or by the contractor as just a preliminary to his own construction project, the jobs coming to the office can be thought of and managed as projects within the office. If each job coming into the office is thought of as a project, good use can be made of the techniques and procedures which have been developed in other fields for project management.

7.5   Project-management Techniques

By far the greatest majority of project-management technology has been based on CPM and PERT, two methodologies formulated in the late 1950s. CPM is the acronym for Critical-Path Method, which was developed in a research program seeking an improved means of planning and scheduling construction projects. The basis of CPM is a network representing the items of work planned to be done in accomplishing the project. With a length of time assigned to each work item, the longest path through the network is a measure of the (shortest) time in which the project can be completed and is thus the "critical path."

PERT, Project Evaluation and Review Technique, was developed for the U.S. Navy as a means of planning and controlling the development of the Polaris Missile System. PERT, like CPM, involves a project network and the calculation of the longest path. That these two outstanding methodologies were developed at about the same time shows the great interest in and demand for project-management technology. The fact that separate groups developing means of controlling two very different kinds of work came up with solutions so similar in concept shows that the same technology of project management can be applied in many different areas of work.

The main difference between CPM and PERT as originally formulated was in the means of estimating lengths of time required to accomplish the work items. CPM, developed for building construction, was intended to be used in projects where the project planner was familiar from past experience with the type of work being done and could estimate accurately the time required for each item of work. PERT, on the other hand, was developed to control a project in which much research and innovation was involved, where time estimates were very difficult to make accurately. But since their development, CPM and PERT have been added to and modified so much that among the many versions of both in use now, the two names have lost much of the original distinction.

As many new procedures and techniques of project management have been developed from and added to CPM and PERT, a great number of specialized names and terms have come to be used. In addition to the descriptive name telling what a project-management technique does, most techniques are called by acronyms given by the developers and users. To avoid confusion, descriptive names will be used for techniques and procedures presented in this chapter.

Of the many individual project-management techniques and procedures being used, the great majority are used in one of the three major phases of project management: *planning* a schedule, *allocating* costs and resources, and *controlling* the work of the project. In more detail, these three main areas of project management are:

1. Planning and scheduling the work by using a network model representing the items of work, their interdependencies, and the estimated duration of each work item.

2. Developing feasible patterns of cost flow and resource usage by tying cost inflows and outflows to points in the network and by assigning required resources to work items and then making possible schedule adjustments on the basis of cost flow and resource usage patterns. Resources in the professional office would be primarily the manpower available for the project.

3. Controlling the implementation of the project by modifying the project network on the basis of work done, costs incurred, and changes in the work plan, and then working on the basis of the updated schedule.

Because of the limited scope of this chapter, just a few project-management techniques will be presented. The techniques included are those readily applicable in the context of the architectural-engineering office and essential to a basic understanding of the three phases of project-management technology. For someone interested in looking more deeply into project management a number of textbooks are available.

7.6   The Project Network

The basic element in project-management technology is the project network, a representation of the work to be done in implementing the project. The work planned to implement the project is broken down into separate items of work called activities. These activities are shown graphically as an interconnected network. A network is a directed graph, a configuration of arrows and nodes, with the interconnections of the arrows showing the interdependencies between the activities. Figure 7.1 shows a network with three nodes and three arrows. The three nodes 1, 2, and 3 are the blocks with the numbers in them. The three arrows 1–2, 2–3, and 1–3 are designated by the numbers of the nodes which they connect.

Although project networks are called by different names, there are actually just three different network formats. All three network types are similar, and all use the same calculation procedure for determining the longest path. They differ more in name than in essence. The term "network scheduling" is used here to cover project scheduling with any of the three types of networks.

The three network types are (1) the activity-on-arrow network, (2) the activity-on-node network, and (3) the event-oriented network. This third type, the event-oriented network, is used mostly in projects where the work items cannot be clearly spelled out, such as research and development programs, and would not be so useful in the architectural-engineering office. The difference in the two activity-oriented network types is in the way that the network elements, the arrows and nodes, are used to represent the work items.

The network format traditionally used has been the activity-on-arrow type, where the activities are represented by the arrows and the interdependencies of the activities are shown by the way in which the arrows are interconnected. The activity interdependencies follow the rule that an activity represented by an arrow going out of a node may not begin until all the activities represented by arrows coming into that node have been completed. The activity-on-arrow network shown in Fig. 7.2 shows the situation where activity C cannot begin until activities A and B have been completed.

The activity-on-node network has been developed more recently and

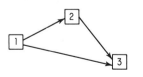

Fig. 7.1 Network with three nodes and three arrows

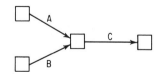

Fig. 7.2 Activity-on-arrow network

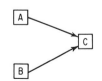

Fig. 7.3 Activity-on-node network

is now coming into wide use. This network type is called by a variety of different names, such as circle-arrow or precedence diagram. The more descriptive name activity-on-node will be used here because it identifies the characteristic difference between the two activity-oriented network types. As the name activity-on-node implies, the activities in the project are represented by the nodes, or blocks, of the network, and the interdependencies between the activities are represented by the arrows connecting the corresponding nodes. The interdependency rule for the activity-on-node network is that an activity may not begin until the activities at the tails of all arrows coming into the activity have been completed. Figure 7.3 is the activity-on-node representation of a situation where activity C may not begin until activities A and B have been completed.

Either of these two network types can be used to represent the same project, and the calculations involved are quite similar. Thus the choice of one or the other is largely a matter of preference and judgment. Work with both types of these networks usually leads to choosing the activity-on-node network. The main reason for continued use of the activity-on arrow network form seems to be force of habit and reluctance to go through the retraining involved in changing. A major advantage of the activity-on-node type is that it is conceptually clearer and is easier to explain to someone who is first learning to work with a project network. There are no "dummy" activities to be explained as part of the activity-on-node network, which requires only one type of arrow to show the interdependencies. Another advantage of the activity-on-node network is that a network is easier to draw up than with an activity-on-arrow network. A third advantage of the activity-on-node network is that there are three additional interdependency relationships which can be used to give a more accurate representation of a real work plan. The activity-on-node network allows nodes to be treated as events (particular points in time) just as does the activity-on-arrow network format.

Although PROJECT, the problem-oriented language described in Secs. 7.10 to 7.12, will handle any of the three network types, the examples will be worked out with the activity-on-node network.

The network shown in Fig. 7.4 is an example of how the activity-on-node network might be used to represent a job in the architectural-engineering office. The nodes representing work items, or activities, are drawn as boxes with the activity description written inside them. The circles are nodes representing events, stages, or points in time which occur in the job when certain groups of activities have been completed.

The project network, shown up to now only in terms of items of work with their interdependencies, becomes much more useful when the dimen-

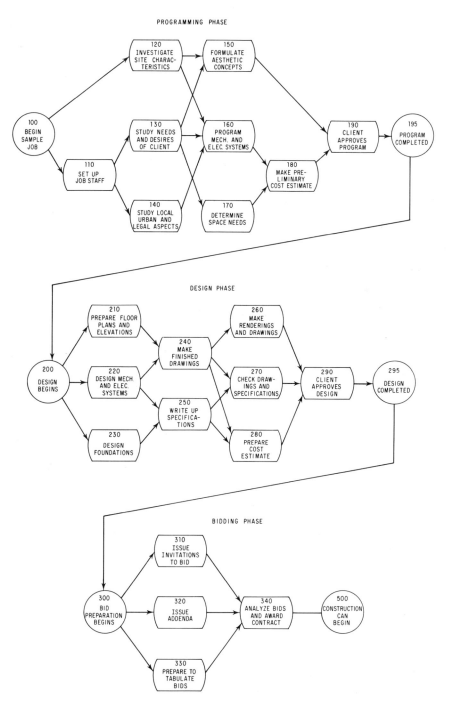

Fig. 7.4 Project network for an office job

sion of time is added. This is done by estimating for each activity a duration, the time required to perform the work represented by the activity. When durations have been assigned to all the activities, some very useful information can be derived from a series of rather straightforward calculations made on the basis of the network.

The information which can be calculated from a network having activity durations amounts to a planning schedule. This includes:

1. The time necessary to complete the project

2. Identification of "critical" activities, those activities which if delayed will cause the entire project to be delayed by the same amount of time

3. The time at which each critical activity must be started and completed

4. The earliest and latest time that the other ("noncritical") activities may be started and completed without delaying completion of the project

7.7   Resources and Costs

A very important factor in scheduling the work in an architectural-engineering office is the work load on the office personnel—the designers, engineers, and draftsmen. The work load on these skilled personnel, when they are considered in project-management terms as types of resources, can be very effectively planned ahead of time by using project-management techniques for resource allocation and scheduling.

Resource scheduling can be done for any number of types of resources, in this case the types of office personnel. To perform resource scheduling for office personnel, the number of each personnel type required to complete each activity in its estimated duration must be estimated. Using the network calculations, each activity is linked to a time period in scheduling the job in the office. When the resources being considered are linked to activities, the resources being used can be, through the activities, also linked to time. This will give for each personnel type being considered a rate of usage over the job's duration. These rates of resource usage over a time period show up very well when plotted as a histogram or graph. Figure 7.5 shows the number of designer-hours required for each day of a project.

Project-management resource-scheduling techniques can be used to adjust the job schedule so that (1) planned work loads will stay under given limits, and (2) the work loads will be "leveled," or spread as evenly as possible in keeping with time limits put on the job's completion.

The calculations involved in resource scheduling are very repetitive and in some cases require several trials before an acceptable solution is obtained. This sort of calculation is hardly possible to do by hand but can

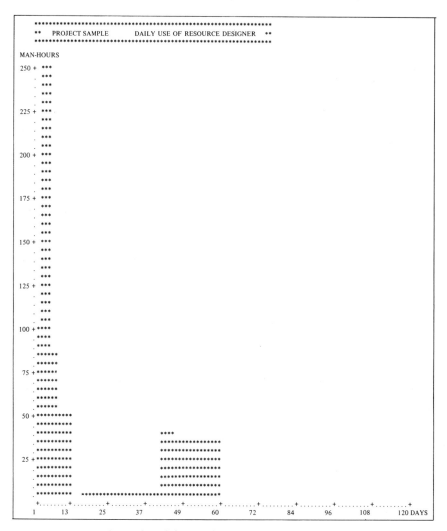

Fig. 7.5   **The number of designer-hours required on each day of an office job**

be used effectively when a computer is available to perform the calculations quickly and cheaply.

Just as linking any resource to the activities using it will tie the use of that resource to time, linking the inflow and outflow of cash with activities and events in the network will establish the time pattern of cash flow. The knowledge of this forecast pattern of cash flow can be very useful to office accountants in looking ahead to office expenses and payments as well as to office management in deciding when other jobs must or must not be taken. A plot of the rate of costs over the duration of the office job(s) is

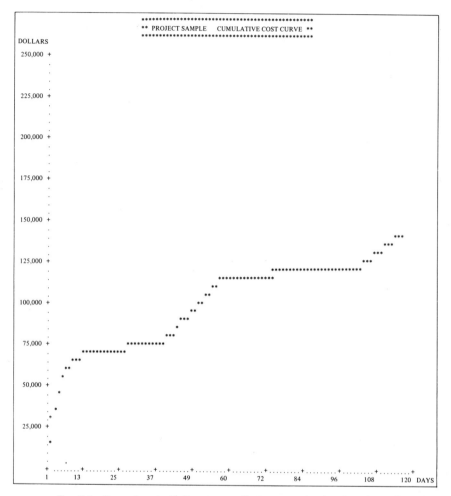

Fig. 7.6   **Forecast cost of office personnel's time over the duration of an office job**

very meaningful to office management. Figure 7.6 shows a forecast of costs of the time of designers, engineers, and draftsmen over the duration of an office job.

7.8   Multiproject Management

Managing the work load on office personnel requires keeping track of the combined effects of all the jobs under way in the office. Most of the use made of project-management techniques in architectural-engineering offices to date has been only use of the network to schedule individual jobs, without tying the jobs together. While in most cases the interdependencies of the activities do not carry over from network to network, the work load on office personnel and the office costs do show the effects of all the jobs which might be underway. This means that use of project-management techniques for more than just scheduling the work of individual jobs requires that all current jobs must be handled as one to make effective use of the techniques for cost and resource scheduling.

In project-management terms, this makes the management of the architectural-engineering office a problem of multiproject management, where management decisions must be based on the combined effects of several projects going on at the same time. To be able to use the project-management techniques particularly helpful in the architectural-engineering office, the office should choose a computer-based project-management system which operates in a multiproject context.

7.9 Updating the Network

The value of using a project network continues throughout the life of the project if the network is kept updated to reflect changes. As work is done on the project and as parts of the work plan are changed, the network is no longer an accurate representation of the work to be done in implementing the project if the network is not updated and modified to reflect these changes. Without continuing modification, the activities and their interrelationships in the network will differ more and more from the work to be done. Inaccuracies in the reports based on the network will eventually increase until a point is reached where these reports are no longer useful and at times are even misleading.

When an item on a network is modified, the network calculations must be made again to ensure that the network-based reports are based on the latest network status. This recalculation is very burdensome; thus updating is another project-management phase where a computer is almost indispensable. Many times an inexperienced project manager, working without computer support, has resolved to keep the network updated and recalculated. But the recalculation by hand is so tedious and expensive in terms of man-hours needed that the vows to update and recalculate usually lead first to the use of inaccurate networks for reports and then often to the abandonment of the project network soon after the initial planning phase.

A network is a very useful tool in initially planning and scheduling a job. The planner must explicitly state each step (activity) in the job and then estimate the time to be taken to complete each step. Using the network interdependencies, the calculations made give a more accurate and more complete job schedule than would be estimated otherwise. The network, when updated to reflect both planning changes and work accomplished, can be a powerful tool for comparing the actual job progress with planned progress. This is a great help to the manager in controlling the job.

This short discussion of project-management technology has covered some of the phases and techniques of project management which could be used effectively in the architectural-engineering office. The remainder of this chapter shows how one computer-based system of project-management techniques and procedures might be used in the office.

7.10   PROJECT, A Problem-oriented Language

An example of how project-management techniques might be used in the professional office is shown here with a demonstration of the problem-oriented language PROJECT.* While several other project-management systems are available, none of them is in the form of a problem-oriented language, the aspect of PROJECT which makes it so well suited to use in the architectural-engineering office.

PROJECT has quite a number of useful features, but for illustration here just the simplest and most direct capabilities of PROJECT are demonstrated. After becoming familiar with the commands and features of PROJECT which are shown here, the interested reader will be able to learn and use its more sophisticated and convenient options. PROJECT is explained thoroughly in Reference 3.

To use PROJECT, one must be able to specify the desired operation with the PROJECT commands. Because these commands are made up of simple project-management terms, the office personnel can soon learn to use the computer programs of PROJECT without having to work through a data-processing specialist as an intermediary, which is certainly an advantage to the architectural-engineering office.

Each PROJECT command is a phrase which has three components: the operation name, the data identifier, and the object phrase. The operation name is a verb, in the imperative mood, indicating the desired operation.

---

* PROJECT, an acronym for Project Engineering Control Techniques, is a problem-oriented computer language used for project management. It was developed in the Department of Civil Engineering at M.I.T. as a part of ICES, a large research program dedicated to using the computer to advance the teaching and practice of civil engineering. Further information about ICES, Integrated Civil Engineering System, can be found in Reference 4.

The operation names used in the example are STORE, PRINT, PLOT, and ASSIGN. The data identifier indicates the (data of the) project with which the operation is to be performed. The object phrase indicates the item upon which the operation will be performed and describes any particular way in which the operation is to be performed.

A sample PROJECT command is

STORE 'SAMPLE' NETWORK DATA

The operation name here is STORE, which indicates that data are to be stored. The data identifier is 'SAMPLE,' which indicates that the data to be stored are associated with the project identified as SAMPLE. The object phrase here is NETWORK DATA, indicating that the data to be stored are data describing a project network.

With most of the PROJECT commands which call for information to be printed out, two optional features, SELECT and SORT, may be incorporated into the object phrase of the command to give the user control of the amount and arrangement of information being printed out. The use of the SELECT option allows information relative to just a specified group of selected activities to be printed out in various reports. This overcomes the problem of having a report consisting of many pages of information when information is desired for just a small group of activities. Activities may be specified either by listing them separately in the command or by giving one or more characteristics which they share. The SORT option allows the user to specify an order in which the information printed out is to be arranged. Either or both of the SELECT and SORT options may be used when printing out information relative to activities. Both these options were used to get the print-out shown in Fig. 7.10.

To keep within the scope of the chapter, the illustrative example here includes the use of PROJECT in just two phases of project management, network scheduling and resource allocation. Not included in the example are the PROJECT command REPORT, which is used to report progress and update the network data, and the commands ADD, DELETE, and CHANGE, which can be used to modify the network data.

The project used in the example here is the architectural-engineering job called SAMPLE, which was shown in network form in Fig. 7.4 and from which the information in Figs. 7.5 and 7.6 was taken. This sample project is used for illustration and is not broken down into great detail. It is estimated that, for the project-management techniques to be used effectively, an office job should be broken down into something like 100 or more activities, depending upon the scope of the job.

7.11   Network Scheduling
with PROJECT

This section shows how PROJECT is used to accomplish network scheduling, the first phase of project management, which was discussed above. The information needed for network scheduling is shown graphically in Fig. 7.4 in the form of an activity-on-node project network. When the scheduling calculations are to be made by hand, the network is required since the network is the form on which the calculations are usually made.

On the other hand, when calculations are to be made by computer it is not necessary to make up a network. While the same "network data" must be gathered and while the project network is a familiar form for displaying this information graphically, it can be a time-saver to put the data as they are gathered directly into the tabular form in which they will be put into the computer. Once these data have been gathered and put into the computer, there are computer programs which will have the computer quickly print out a network diagram, possibly a time-scaled diagram.

The information in the network of Fig. 7.4 is shown in Fig. 7.7 in tabular

Number	Description	Duration	Depends upon
100	BEGIN SAMPLE JOB		
110	SET UP JOB STAFF	2	100
120	INVESTIGATE SITE CHARACTERISTICS	5	100
130	STUDY NEEDS AND DESIRES OF CLIENT	6	110
140	STUDY LOCAL URBAN AND LEGAL ASPECTS	3	110
150	FORMULATE AESTHETIC CONCEPTS	4	120, 130
160	PROGRAM MECH. AND ELEC. SYSTEMS	2	120, 130, 140
170	DETERMINE SPACE NEEDS	4	130
180	MAKE PRELIMINARY COST ESTIMATE	1	160, 170
190	CLIENT APPROVES PROGRAM	2	150, 180
195	PROGRAM COMPLETED	------	190
200	DESIGN BEGINS	------	195
210	PREPARE FLOOR PLANS AND ELEVATIONS	30	200
220	DESIGN MECH. AND ELEC. SYSTEMS	25	200
230	DESIGN FOUNDATIONS	10	200
240	MAKE FINISHED DRAWINGS	30	210, 220
250	WRITE UP SPECIFICATIONS	20	220, 230
260	MAKE RENDERINGS AND DRAWINGS	25	240
270	CHECK DRAWINGS AND SPECIFICATIONS	5	240, 250
280	PREPARE COST ESTIMATE	4	240, 250
290	CLIENT APPROVES DESIGN	5	260, 270, 280
295	DESIGN COMPLETED	------	290
300	BID PREPARATION BEGINS	------	295
310	ISSUE INVITATIONS TO BID	5	300
320	ISSUE ADDENDA	5	300
330	PREPARE TO TABULATE BIDS	4	300
340	ANALYZE BIDS AND AWARD CONTRACT	10	310, 320, 330
500	CONSTRUCTION CAN BEGIN	------	340

Fig. 7.7   Precedence table for an office job

form as a "precedence table," which can be made up directly as data are gathered.

A precedence table contains a list of the numbers and descriptions of all the activities and events of the job. Estimated duration is shown for each of the activities. The interdependencies between the activities (and events) are shown in a precedence table by listing, for each activity and event, the activities and events upon which it is directly dependent. In the precedence table of Fig. 7.7 no dependencies are entered for event 100, showing that it does not depend upon any of the other activities or events. This is shown in the network of Fig. 7.4 by the fact that event 100 has no dependency arrows coming into it. In the network there is a dependency arrow corresponding to each dependency entry in the precedence table. The precedence table shows that activity 130 depends directly upon activity 110, and this means that in the network there is an arrow going from activity 110 to activity 130.

A preprinted, standard precedence table would be very useful for project management in the architectural-engineering office where jobs are usually similar in that most of the same steps are taken in each job, varying in the time required because of the size of the job and the office staff available. A standard, preprinted table would have a list of typical activities and events as well as several blank spaces in case a job would involve special steps (or activities). The duration column could be left blank and then filled in for each job. The normal dependencies could be printed in, to be modified if a particular job had some different arrangement of steps. It is more practical to have a standard precedence table rather than a standard network, for a precedence table can be modified much more conveniently to suit each job than could a network diagram. Then the data could be taken directly from the precedence table and input into the computer to perform the calculations and to draw up a network, if a network is desired.

Using the PROJECT command STORE 'SAMPLE' NETWORK DATA, which was explained in Sec. 7.10, the information from the precedence table of Fig. 7.7 can be used to store the network data in the computer system. Once the network data have been stored for this project, they can be referred to time and time again without needing to be resubmitted. When the project has been completed, the data can be removed from the computer system by using the command

REMOVE 'SAMPLE' NETWORK DATA

Figure 7.8 shows the arrangement of punched cards used to input the data for the sample job, given here the name 'SAMPLE.' It should be noted that the arrangement of network data input with PROJECT is similar to the precedence table of Fig. 7.7. When the dollar sign is used on a data card it causes the card to be ignored by the computer system. Thus cards with dollar signs as the first item punched on them can be used, as in Fig. 7.8, to insert various comments and labels to make the input data more readable. The words "DEPENDS UPON," which identify the precedences for each activity, may be abbreviated to "DEP" or just "D" for convenience.

```
STORE 'SAMPLE' NETWORK DATA
$        PRECEDENCE TABLE FOR JOB IN A-E OFFICE
$
$        *************************************************************************************
$
$ NUMBER       DESCRIPTION                          DURATION     DEPENDENCIES
$
$              *** PROGRAMMING PHASE ***
100      'BEGIN SAMPLE JOB'
110      'SET UP JOB STAFF'                             2        DEPENDS UPON 100
120      'INVESTIGATE SITE CHARACTERISTICS'             5        DEPENDS UPON 100
130      'STUDY NEEDS AND DESIRES OF CLIENT'            6        DEPENDS UPON 110
140      'STUDY LOCAL URBAN AND LEGAL ASPECTS'          3        DEP 110
150      'FORMULATE AESTHETIC CONCEPTS'                 4        DEP 120, 130
160      'PROGRAM MECH. AND ELEC. SYSTEMS'             2        D 120, 130, 140
170      'DETERMINE SPACE NEEDS'                        4        D 130
180      'MAKE PRELIMINARY COST ESTIMATE'               1        D 160, 170
190      '**CLIENT APPROVES PROGRAM**'                  2        D 150, 180
195      'PROGRAM COMPLETED'                            0        DEP 190
$
$              *** DESIGN PHASE ***
200      'DESIGN BEGINS'                                         DEPENDS UPON 195
210      'PREPARE FLOOR PLANS AND ELEVATIONS'          30        D 200
220      'DESIGN MECH. AND ELEC. SYSTEMS'              25        D 200
230      'DESIGN FOUNDATIONS'                          10        D 200
240      'MAKE FINISHED DRAWINGS'                      30        D 210, 220
250      'WRITE UP SPECIFICATIONS'                     20        D 220, 230
260      'MAKE RENDERINGS AND MODELS'                  25        DEP 240
270      'CHECK DRAWINGS AND SPECIFICATIONS'            5        DEP 240, 250
280      'PREPARE COST ESTIMATE'                        4        DEP 240, 250
290      '**CLIENT APPROVES DESIGN**'                   5        DEP 260, 270, 280
295      'DESIGN COMPLETED'                                      DEP 290
$
$              *** BIDDING PHASE ***
300      'BID PREPARATION BEGINS'                                DEP 295
310      'ISSUE INVITATIONS TO BID'                     5        DEP 300
320      'ISSUE ADDENDA'                                5        DEP 300
330      'PREPARE TO TABULATE BIDS'                     4        DEP 300
340      'ANALYZE BIDS AND AWARD CONTRACT'             10        DEP 310, 320, 330
500      'CONSTRUCTION CAN BEGIN'                                DEP 340
LAST ACTIVITY
```

Fig. 7.8 Network data for input with PROJECT

Once the network data for project 'SAMPLE' have been stored, the PROJECT command

PRINT 'SAMPLE' NETWORK DATA

can be used to get a copy of the network data to be used for checking the data or as a record. And also now the project schedule can be calculated, and the command

PRINT 'SAMPLE' PLANNING SCHEDULE

can be used to get the schedule shown in Fig. 7.9.

The reader should note that the schedule in Fig. 7.9 does not give a specific time for each activity to start and finish. Instead, it gives for each activity "early" and "late" start and finish times, which define a time period in which the activity could be started and finished without causing the completion of the project to be delayed. This planning schedule is a basis for planning specific start and finish times for the activities. Once specific start and finish times have been assigned to activities, either by the project manager or automatically by the programs of PROJECT, this information is shown in a "working schedule." The specific start and finish times for each activity are assigned in one of three ways, explicitly by the project manager, implicitly based on resource constraints given by the project manager, or assumed by the PROJECT programs as the earliest possible start and finish times. A working schedule is shown in Fig. 7.10, where the SELECT option has been used to include just the activities starting before August 15 and the SORT option has been used to put these activities in chronological order of their starting dates.

7.12   Office Resources

The management of the architectural-engineering office is dominated by the problem of how best to assign the office professionals and skilled technicians to work on the jobs coming into the office. If the valuable time of the office staff is considered to be expensive resources, then the project-management techniques for resource allocation can be a great help in forecasting and managing the work loads on office personnel.

The techniques for resource allocation, comprising the second phase of project management, use data calculated in network scheduling as well as additional information dealing with the resources. This supplemental resource information is data both about the resources themselves, such as names, costs, and limitations on their use, as well as telling how many units of each resource are to be used to accomplish each activity. This resource information is input to the computer system with PROJECT in a manner similar to the way in which the network data are input and there-

PROJECT DURATION IS 120 WORK DAYS, WORK WEEK IS 5 DAYS
WORK IS SCHEDULED TO START ON 3 JUN 1968 AND TO BE COMPLETED ON 15 NOV 1968.

EVENT SCHEDULE
****

	EVENT	DESCRIPTION	EARLY TIME	LATE TIME
C	100	BEGIN SAMPLE JOB	3 JUN 1968 1	3 JUN 1968 1
C	195	PROGRAM COMPLETED	24 JUN 1968 16	24 JUN 1968 16
C	200	DESIGN BEGINS	24 JUN 1968 16	24 JUN 1968 16
C	295	DESIGN COMPLETED	28 OCT 1968 106	28 OCT 1968 106
C	300	BID PREPARATION BEGINS	28 OCT 1968 106	28 OCT 1968 106
C	500	CONSTRUCTION CAN BEGIN	15 NOV 1968 120	15 NOV 1968 120

END OF EVENT SCHEDULE
****

ACTIVITY SCHEDULE
****

SCHEDULE

START TIMES ARE FIGURED FOR THE MORNING OF THE WORK DAY
FINISH TIMES ARE FIGURED FOR THE EVENING OF THE WORK DAY
ACTIVITIES ARE SORTED ACCORDING TO NODE NUMBERS
'C' IN MARGIN DESIGNATES A CRITICAL ACTIVITY

	ACTIVITY	DESCRIPTION	DURA-TION	EARLY START	LATE START	EARLY FINISH	LATE FINISH	FREE FLOAT	TOTAL FLOAT
C	110	SET UP JOB STAFF	2	3JUN68 1	3JUN68 1	4JUN68 2	4JUN68 2	0	0
		PRECEDES ACTIVITY 130 140							
	120	INVESTIGATE SITE CHARACTERISTICS	5	3JUN68 1	7JUN68 5	7JUN68 5	13JUN68 9	3	4
		PRECEDES ACTIVITY 150 160							

164

	Activity	Description / Precedes	Precedes Activity	Duration	Earliest Start	Earliest Finish	Latest Start	Latest Finish	Slack	Slack
C	130	STUDY NEEDS AND DESIRES OF CLIENT	150 160	6	5JUN68 / 3	5JUN68 / 3	12JUN68 / 8	12JUN68 / 8	0	0
	140	STUDY LOCAL URBAN AND LEGAL ASPECTS	160 170	3	5JUN68 / 3	12JUN68 / 8	7JUN68 / 5	14JUN68 / 10	3	5
	150	FORMULATE AESTHETIC CONCEPTS	190	4	13JUN68 / 9	14JUN68 / 10	18JUN68 / 12	19JUN68 / 13	1	1
	160	PROGRAM MECH. AND ELEC. SYSTEMS	180	2	13JUN68 / 9	17JUN68 / 11	14JUN68 / 10	18JUN68 / 12	2	2
C	170	DETERMINE SPACE NEEDS	180	4	13JUN68 / 9	13JUN68 / 9	18JUN68 / 12	18JUN68 / 12	0	0
C	180	MAKE PRELIMINARY COST ESTIMATE	190	1	19JUN68 / 13	19JUN68 / 13	19JUN68 / 13	19JUN68 / 13	0	0
C	190	**CLIENT APPROVES PROGRAM**	195	2	20JUN68 / 14	20JUN68 / 14	21JUN68 / 15	21JUN68 / 15	0	0
C	210	PREPARE FLOOR PLANS AND ELEVATIONS	240	30	24JUN68 / 16	24JUN68 / 16	2AUG68 / 45	2AUG68 / 45	0	0
	220	DESIGN MECH. AND ELEC. SYSTEMS	240 250	25	24JUN68 / 16	1JUL68 / 21	26JUL68 / 40	2AUG68 / 45	0	5
	230	DESIGN FOUNDATIONS	250	10	24JUN68 / 16	2SEP68 / 66	5JUL68 / 25	13SEP68 / 75	15	50
C	240	MAKE FINISHED DRAWINGS	250	30	5AUG68 / 46	5AUG68 / 46	13SEP68 / 75	13SEP68 / 75	0	0
	250	WRITE UP SPECIFICATIONS	270 280	20	29JUL68 / 41	16SEP68 / 76	23AUG68 / 60	11OCT68 / 95	15	35

ACTIVITY		DESCRIPTION	DURATION	EARLY START	LATE START	EARLY FINISH	LATE FINISH	FREE FLOAT	TOTAL FLOAT
C	260	PRECEDES ACTIVITY 270 280 MAKE RENDERINGS AND MODELS	25	16SEP68 76	16SEP68 76	18OCT68 100	18OCT68 100	0	0
	270	PRECEDES ACTIVITY 290 CHECK DRAWINGS AND SPECIFICATIONS	5	16SEP68 76	14OCT68 96	20SEP68 80	18OCT68 100	20	20
	280	PRECEDES ACTIVITY 290 PREPARE COST ESTIMATE	4	16SEP68 76	15OCT68 97	19SEP68 79	18OCT68 100	21	21
C	290	PRECEDES ACTIVITY 290 **CLIENT APPROVES DESIGN**	5	21OCT68 101	21OCT58 101	25OCT68 105	25OCT68 105	0	0
C	310	PRECEDES ACTIVITY 295 ISSUE INVITATIONS TO BID	5	28OCT68 106	28OCT68 106	1NOV68 110	1NOV68 110	0	0
C	320	PRECEDES ACTIVITY 340 ISSUE ADDENDA	5	28OCT68 106	28OCT68 106	1NOV68 110	1NOV68 110	0	0
	330	PRECEDES ACTIVITY 340 PREPARE TO TABULATE BIDS	4	28OCT68 106	29OCT68 107	31OCT68 109	1NOV68 110	1	1
C	340	PRECEDES ACTIVITY 340 ANALYZE BIDS AND AWARD CONTRACT	10	4NOV68 111	4NOV68 111	15NOV68 120	15NOV68 120	0	0
		PRECEDES ACTIVITY 500							

* END OF SCHEDULE *
****

Fig. 7.9 Planning schedule for project 'SAMPLE'

EVENT WORKING SCHEDULE
****

EVENT OCCURRENCES SHOULD BE RECORDED AS THE WORKDAY FOLLOWING THE DAY THE LAST
OF THE PRECEDING ACTIVITIES IS FINISHED.

	EVENT	DESCRIPTION	SCHEDULED OCCURRENCE	ACTUAL OCCURRENCE
C	100	BEGIN SAMPLE JOB	3 JUN 1968 1	
C	195	PROGRAM COMPLETED	24 JUN 1968 16	
C	200	DESIGN BEGINS	24 JUN 1968 16	

END OF EVENT SCHEDULE
****
ACTIVITY WORKING SCHEDULE
****

ACTIVITY NUMBER(S)	DESCRIPTION	DURATION EST	DURATION ACT	DURATION DEV	START SCH'D	START REP'D	FINISH SCH'D	FINISH REP'D
C 110	SET UP JOB STAFF	2			3JUN68 1		4JUN68 2	
120	INVESTIGATE SITE CHARACTERISTICS	5			3JUN68 1		7JUN68 5	
C 130	STUDY NEEDS AND DESIRES OF CLIENT	6			5JUN68 3		12JUN68 8	
140	STUDY LOCAL URBAN AND LEGAL ASPECTS	3			5JUN68 3		7JUN68 5	
150	FORMULATE AESTHETIC CONCEPTS	4			13JUN68 9		18JUN68 12	
160	PROGRAM MECH. AND ELEC. SYSTEMS	2			13JUN68 9		14JUN68 10	
C 170	DETERMINE SPACE NEEDS	4			13JUN68 9		18JUN 1268	

ACTIVITY		DURATION			START		FINISH	
NUMBER(S)	DESCRIPTION	EST	ACT	DEV	SCH'D	REP'D	SCH'D	REP'D
C	MAKE PRELIMINARY COST ESTIMATE	1			19JUN68		19JUN68	
	180				13		13	
C	**CLIENT APPROVES PROGRAM**	2			20JUN68		21JUN68	
	190				14		15	
C	PREPARE FLOOR PLANS AND ELEVATIONS	30			24JUN68		2AUG68	
	210				16		45	
	DESIGN MECH. AND ELEC. SYSTEMS	25			24JUN68		26JUL68	
	220				16		40	
	DESIGN FOUNDATIONS	10			24JUN68		5JUL68	
	230				16		25	
C	MAKE FINISHED DRAWINGS	30			5AUG68		13SEP68	
	240				46		75	
	WRITE UP SPECIFICATIONS	20			29JUL68		23AUG68	
	250				41		60	

END OF WORKING SCHEDULE
****

Fig. 7.10 Working schedule for project 'SAMPLE'

fore will not be shown in the example here. The manner of inputting resource data with PROJECT is described in Reference 3.

Once the resource data have been input to the computer system, to be used along with the data calculated from network scheduling, the PROJECT commands PRINT and PLOT can be used to get a variety of graphs and tables of daily and cumulative cost and resource usage. The SELECT and SORT options of PROJECT can be used as part of the object phrase of the PRINT and PLOT commands so that the tables and graphs will be based on any desired groups of activities and so that the contents of the tables will be printed out in a convenient arrangement. The graphs shown in Figs. 7.5 and 7.6 are examples of PROJECT output dealing with resources and costs.

The foregoing text and example problem have attempted to introduce the reader to network scheduling in general and to a useful problem-oriented language, PROJECT, in particular. As developments in computer-based management techniques continue, and as projects grow increasingly larger and more complex, it seems quite likely that this phase of office activity will assume increasing importance in office practice.

REFERENCES

1. R. I. Levin and C. A. Kirkpatrick, *Management Planning and Control with PERT-CPM,* McGraw-Hill Book Company, New York, 1966.
2. J. J. Moder and C. R. Phillips, *Project Management with CPM and PERT,* Reinhold Publishing Corporation, New York, 1964.
3. *ICES PROJECT: An Engineering User's Manual,* M.I.T. Department of Civil Engineering, Cambridge, Mass., 1967.
4. *ICES: Concepts and Facilities,* M.I.T. Department of Civil Engineering, Cambridge, Mass., undated.

CHAPTER EIGHT *Architecture*

and the Computer

By Charles B. Thomsen, AIA

The actual and projected uses of computer techniques for design purposes in an architectural office form the basis of this chapter. This area of design problems is perhaps the weakest of all application areas at the moment. Comments on this and what is being done about it are included in the discussion.

Mr. Thomsen is an Associate Partner of Caudill
Rowlett Scott and has been responsible for
developing computer capabilities within the
firm prior to his present position of co-manager
of the CRS New York office. He studied at the
University of Minnesota and was graduated
from the University of Oklahoma. In 1962, he
received a M. Arch. from M.I.T. Mr. Thomsen
is a visiting lecturer and former Assistant
Professor at Rice University. He is also a
member of the New York chapter of the AIA
and serves on the AIA national committee
on research.

8.1 Introductory Remarks

Architects profess a fundamental inclination for innovation, yet they have lagged behind other professions in applying computer techniques. The reasons seem apparent.

First, architectural offices, which are typically small, have lacked the capital necessary for special architectural programming and accompanying personnel training.

Second, architects who apparently lead the thoughts of the profession are primarily interested in the visual world, one which is far easier to handle with a soft pencil and a roll of yellow paper than with alphanumeric computer-implemented simulation.

Third, most architectural design problems, if taken in their entirety, seem too complex to be handled with a computer or any method that requires systematized completeness. Imagine the variables involved in a floor-plan study (space affinities, circulation, structural and mechanical systems, topography, implications on the exterior elevations, etc.). If indeed it is possible to express parts of the problem in terms acceptable for computation, data are often unobtainable or too vast for economical collection.

Those are the reasons why progress has been slow. However, those reasons are dissolving rapidly through energetic work in many active and progressive-minded offices across the country.

Architecture is expanding at full speed and experiencing changes which disturb the traditionally "tweedy" process of the profession. It is becoming clear that if architects are to retain their customary role as artists who consciously express the values of our civilization, it will only be within the restraints of functional performance and realistic cost restrictions demanded by knowledgeable clients. Even if a patron should have unlimited building resources, by those very circumstances his structure could not be a faithful expression of our culture. As an attitude of optimization and efficiency, the concept of economy itself is becoming a valid aesthetic expression.

8.2 Cost Criteria for Design

The computer promises to give architects mastery over the restraints of function and cost. This he requires to perform his art, just as a sculptor must understand the limits of his clay or the strata of his marble block.

Cost is a basic restriction fundamental to all decisions. It is so intimately woven among all design thinking that architects often fail to recognize its prevailing influence. Yet its unwelcome surprises continue to plague them.

Without complete control of this ubiquitous discipline, the higher aspirations of the profession are unobtainable.

Regional variations, price escalation, feedback delays, inaccurate information from contractors, and the fact that each building is a unique assembly of materials combine to make cost estimating fraught with pitfalls. Despite these unavoidable problems, architects themselves are not without blame. Few have systematic approaches. Instead, they concentrate on solving only the functional and sometimes the aesthetic problems. At the root of these problems is the fact that most cost-estimating systems, even the first computer-implemented systems, are "after the fact." They are adequate for estimating the cost of a project only after it is completely designed and all decisions are made. That is too late. Needed is a system which could be used in the late programming or early design stages, not only to define initial cost limitations before major design concepts are established but particularly to produce comparative information for design decisions.

The first approach of Caudill Rowlett Scott to solving these problems is a computer version of its old manual techniques. It produces costs based on a given design. Quantities and definitions of materials are input. The computer retrieves cost data from a file, extends quantities, multiplies quantity times unit cost, and keeps the total (see Figs. 8.1 and 8.2). The advantage over the manual system is not just a substantial time saving, but more importantly the reruns with minor changes are extremely simple, and a finer, more informative breakdown of costs results. However, this is still an "after-the-fact" system.

A second and more complicated approach to cost estimating is one with necessary engineering and geometry routines built in so that an operator can request cost differences based on design-decision variables or performance criteria (i.e., "How much will I save if I reduce the structural span from 50 to 30 feet?" or "How much more would it cost to increase the handling capacity of the elevator system by 3 percent?"). This approach is far more helpful but is accordingly more difficult to create (see Figs. 8.3 and 8.4).

A third approach that holds much promise is used in early schematic design stages before too much is known about the design. It is not an "after-the-fact" system. It is a rudimentary conversation mode which allows a designer or project manager to peck away at the typewriter console for twenty to thirty minutes, winding up not only with a reasonably accurate cost estimate but also with a clear understanding of the relative cost of the various building components (see Figs. 8.5, 8.6, and 8.7).

The process still has many weaknesses. The accuracy of the calculations exceeds the precision of the assumptions. It is still necessary for the

```
COST ESTIMATE
 CAUDILL ROWLETT SCOTT - ARCHITECTS ENGINEERS PLANNERS
 PAGE 1


CAUDILL ROWLETT SCOTT - ARCHITECTS ENGINEERS PLANNERS
MAY 5, 1967
LAREDO JUNIOR COLLEGE - LAREDO TEXAS


AREA FACTOR            -0.080
ESCALATION FACTOR       0.020
COPIT FACTOR            0.250
DEVELOPMENT FACTOR      0.050
```

			NET COST	AREA-ESC COST	W/COPIT COST	W/DEV COST
CODE	ITEM	UNITS				
	EXTERIOR WALL SYSTEM					
1	MASONRY - FACE BRICK 1 SIDE $65./M	SF	1.230	1.154	1.442	1.514
2	MASONRY - FACE BRICK 8 IN. 2 SIDES AVERAGE	SF	2.620	2.458	3.073	3.226
3	MASONRY - VERTICAL REINFORCING MASONRY WALLS	SF	0.100	0.093	0.117	0.123
4	BRICK - BRICK ARCHES & PIERS	EA	0.287	0.269	0.336	0.353
5	BRICK - FACE BRICK PIERS	EA	0.150	0.140	0.175	0.184
6	MASONRY - COMMON BRICK 1 SIDE AVERAGE	SF	1.070	1.004	1.255	1.317
7	MASONRY - CONCRETE BLOCK LT WT 8IN	SF	0.930	0.872	1.090	1.145
11	WATERPROOFING - WALL DAMPPROOFING	SF	0.100	0.093	0.117	0.123
12	WATERPROOFING - WALL BASE WATERPROOFING	SF	0.270	0.253	0.316	0.332
18	ZONOLITE IN CONCRETE BLOCK WALLS - 8IN	SF	0.120	0.112	0.140	0.147
29	WINDOW WALL - STORE FRONT W/DURANODIC FIN & SOLAR BRONZE GL	SF	5.340	5.011	6.263	6.577
33	DOORS - MEDIUM STYLE ENTRANCE - ALUMINUM STANDARD 6X7	PR	420.000	394.127	492.659	517.292
34	DOORS - MEDIUM STYLE ENTRANCE - ALUMINUM STANDARD 3X7	EA	235.000	220.523	275.654	289.437
36	DOORS - WEATHERSTRIPPING	EA	11.000	10.322	12.902	13.548
39	DOORS - HOLLOW METAL 6FT X 7FT	PR	117.000	109.792	137.240	144.103
40	DOORS - HOLLOW METAL 3FT X 7FT	EA	61.000	57.242	71.552	75.130
44	DOORS - HOLLOW METAL DOOR FRAME - 6FT X 7FT	EA	32.000	30.028	37.536	39.412
46	DOORS - HOLLOW METAL DOOR FRAME - 3FT X 7FT	EA	28.000	26.275	32.844	34.486
47	HARDWARE - PANIC HARDWARE PAIR	PR	228.000	213.955	267.443	280.816
48	HARDWARE - PANIC HARDWARE SINGLE	EA	105.000	98.531	123.164	129.323
49	HARDWARE - EXTERIOR NORMAL DOOR	EA	40.000	37.535	46.919	49.265
50	HARDWARE - DOOR CLOSER - CONCEALED	EA	85.000	79.764	99.705	104.690
51	HARDWARE - REMOVABLE MULL	EA	20.000	18.767	23.459	24.632
53	METAL THRESHOLD - ALUMINUM	LF	4.500	4.222	5.278	5.542
56	EXTERIOR CAULKING - R.B.C.	LS	0.015	0.014	0.017	0.018
57	CONTROL JOINT - EXTERIOR	LF	2.500	2.345	2.932	3.079
58	CONTROL JOINT - INTERIOR	LF	1.000	0.938	1.173	1.231
59	REINFORCING FOR PILASTER	LB	0.140	0.131	0.164	0.172
60	PILASTER CONCRETE	CF	3.000	2.815	3.518	3.694

Fig. 8.1   The quantity takeoff estimating system operates as follows: A basic master data file is built which includes all building materials to be used on the project. The net cost is a national average. It is adjusted according to the following: 1. Area Factor. Adjusts national cost averages to a specific location. 2. Escalation Factor. Anticipates the cost increases at some future time. 3. COPIT Factor. Includes the contractor's overhead, profit, insurance, and taxes. 4. Development Factor. Includes contingencies, site conditions, local taxes, bidding climate, etc. The final cost, of course, is the realistic one. Thus material number one on the top line, Masonry in place, is $1.51 per square foot rather than $1.23 per square foot.

operator to understand basic price data. A quicker technique would be to have the machine retrieve cost data from an internal file. Better yet, performance criteria should be input which would call forth a list of systems from which one could be selected.

Another basic weakness in an all-automated cost-estimating system is that the building geometry must be input in some form so that the quantity of materials may be internally calculated. Measuring this takes time. Hopefully, graphic data processing may soon ease this procedure.

In spite of these weaknesses, this last simple-minded little program is astonishingly helpful. In a few minutes a conscientious designer can save considerable dollars or at least spend the same funds more effectively.

COST ESTIMATE
CAUDILL ROWLETT SCOTT - ARCHITECTS ENGINEERS PLANNERS
PAGE 7

288	CONCRETE BLOCK 6IN	SF	850.00	1.03	879.39	FIRST FLOOR
288	CONCRETE BLOCK 6IN	SF	800.00	1.03	827.66	SECOND FLOOR
289	CONCRETE BLOCK 8IN	SF	840.00	1.14	962.16	FIRST FLOOR
289	CONCRETE BLOCK 8IN	SF	300.00	1.14	343.63	SECOND FLOOR
311	FIREPROOFING COLUMNS	SF	1296.00	1.10	1436.59	FIRST FLOOR
311	FIREPROOFING COLUMNS	SF	1080.00	1.10	1197.16	SECOND FLOOR
312	DRY WALL - DOUBLE 2-1/2 METAL STUD PARTITION W/5/8 DRY WAL	SF	3400.00	1.10	3768.84	FIRST FLOOR
312	DRY WALL - DOUBLE 2-1/2 METAL STUD PARTITION W/5/8 DRY WAL	SF	2520.00	1.10	2793.38	SECOND FLOOR
313	DRY WALL - 5/8IN GYPSUM BOARD - SCREWED	SF	1550.00	0.19	305.44	FIRST FLOOR
313	DRY WALL - 5/8IN GYPSUM BOARD - SCREWED	SF	2350.00	0.19	463.10	SECOND FLOOR
315	DRY WALL-5/8IN GYP BRD-2 SIDES & 3-5/8IN METAL STUD STRIGHT	SF	2200.00	0.83	1842.54	FIRST FLOOR
315	DRY WALL-5/8IN GYP BRD-2 SIDES & 3-5/8IN METAL STUD STRIGHT	SF	3470.00	0.83	2906.20	SECOND FLOOR
320	FRAMES W/1/4IN CLEAR PP GLASS -SIDELITE DOOR	SF	270.00	3.10	838.01	FIRST FLOOR
320	FRAMES W/1/4IN CLEAR PP GLASS -SIDELITE DOOR	SF	250.00	3.10	775.93	SECOND FLOOR
338	TOILET STALL W/DOOR - METAL - BAKED ENAMEL	EA	12.00	129.32	1551.87	
354	INSULATION - 1IN RIGID BOARD INSUL W/MESH FOR SOUND CONTROL	SF	940.00	0.45	428.36	
356	WOOD FURRING STRIPS - NAILABLE SURFACE 2FT OC	SF	1550.00	0.09	152.72	FIRST FLOOR
356	WOOD FURRING STRIPS - NAILABLE SURFACE 2FT OC	SF	2050.00	0.09	201.99	SECOND FLOOR
361	CERAMIC TILE - GLAZED MORTAR SETTING BED	SF	800.00	2.18	1744.01	FIRST FLOOR
361	CERAMIC TILE - GLAZED MORTAR SETTING BED	SF	1150.00	2.18	2507.02	SECOND FLOOR
362	CHALK BOARDS - COMPOSITION TYPE W/TRIM TRAY & GROUNDS	SF	2304.00	2.34	5391.66	
363	TACK BOARD - VINYL FABRIC ON 1/2IN FIBER BOARD W/TRIM	SF	1088.00	1.90	2077.05	
366	BASE - 4IN RESILIENT BASE	LF	1627.00	0.43	701.36	FIRST FLOOR
366	BASE - 4IN RESILIENT BASE	LF	1895.00	0.43	816.89	SECOND FLOOR
369	BASE - CERAMIC TILE BASE	LF	200.00	2.09	418.76	
	SUBTOTAL		35331.81			
	COST PER SQ. FT		1.13			
	METAL SPECIALITIES					
388	HAND RAIL - STANDING - WOOD	LF	56.00	11.08	620.75	
390	HAND RAIL - WALL MOUNT - WOOD	LF	56.00	6.95	389.69	
396	METAL FLOOR TRENCH COVER & FRAME WITH KALMAN TOPPING	LF	87.00	11.39	991.16	
403	WALL ACCESS DOORS 12IN X 12IN	EA	4.00	16.01	64.04	
406	METAL SCREENS INCLUDING FRAMES	SF	80.00	1.47	118.23	
407	MISCELLANEOUS IRON & BOLTS	SF	31250.00	0.11	3464.01	
	SUBTOTAL		5647.91			
	COST PER SQ. FT.		0.18			
	PAINTING AND FINISHING					
415	PAINTING - DOORS, PANELS & FRAMES 125 SF/EA	SF	7125.00	0.18	1316.32	
417	PAINTING - MASONRY	SF	13150.00	0.17	2267.46	
418	PAINTING - GYPSUM BOARD & TAPE & FLOAT	SF	27900.00	0.20	5841.71	
420	PAINTING - FRAMES W/GLASS	SF	520.00	0.12	64.04	
421	PAINTING - MISC IRON & METALS	TN	15.00	32.02	480.34	
423	PAINTING - MILLWORK	LS	250.00	1.23	307.91	
427	SPECIAL SURFACE EFFECTS - SANDBLASTING - LIGHT	SF	875.00	0.30	269.42	
	SUBTOTAL		10547.22			
	COST PER SQ. FT		0.33			
	MISCELLANEOUS ITEMS					
449	MILLWORK - JANITOR SHELVING	LF	200.00	0.80	160.11	
456	CARPENTRY - WOOD BLOCKING BRACING & ETC	SF	31250.00	0.03	1154.67	
457	GRAPHICS - CAST ALUMINUM PLAQUE	EA	1.00	187.21	187.21	

Fig. 8.2   The takeoff is carefully listed with the quantity of material, price location, and cost printed as independent numbers. Subtotals for each building system are developed.

But while this problem and other cost-estimating programs are helpful in themselves, they are only a fragment of a broader program which will become a true design system.

8.3   Design Systems

It is not yet clear how architects will construct their computer-implemented design systems. Early approaches to the computer resulted in "black-box programs." Black-box programs must have all possible design conditions described and all possible solutions anticipated. Input is gathered and entered, all processes are automatic, and the answer results without operator intervention. Yet there will always be considerations

ELEVATOR DESIGN PROGRAM

COST DATA INPUT JAN 1967 - INCLUDES COPIT.
COSTS ARE FOR PURPOSES OF DESIGN SELECTION NOT PROJECT ESTIMATING.
INCLUDE A DECIMAL IN ALL ANSWERS.
DONT USE ALPHABETIC CHARACTERS. DEPRESS EOF AFTER EACH ANSWER.
ESTABLISH BASIC DESIGN CRITERIA. TYPE ANSWER AFTER EACH CRITERIA.
IF YOU MAKE AN ERROR TYPE 9999. FOR NEXT ANSWER.

1. WAITING TIME (30. SEC MAX IS USUAL)
    25.

2. HANDLING CAPACITY (.15 X POPULATION IN 5 MIN IS USUAL).
    .125

3. BUILDING DENSITY (125. NET RENTABLE SQ FT PER PERSON IS USUAL)
    150.

4. ANTICIPATED FLOOR TO FLOOR DIMENSION (IN FT AND TENTHS OF FT, IE. 12.5).
    12.5

    ANTICIPATED GROUND TO 2ND FLOOR DISTANCE.
    20.5

5. TOTAL NO. OF FLOORS (INCL GND FL)
    8.

6. ZONES (TOTAL NUMBER).
    1.

9. AVERAGE NET RENTABLE SQ FT PER FLOOR.

    14000.

THE LEAST EXPENSIVE SYSTEM WHICH WILL MEET DESIGN CRITERIA IS
4 - 300 FOOT PER MIN 2000 LB ELEVATORS.
THE ESTIMATED HANDLING CAPACITY IS
0.19 TIMES THE POPULATION IN 5 MIN.
THE MAXIMUM ESTIMATED WAITING TIME IS 23.8 SECONDS.
TOTAL ESTIMATED COST = 124800.01
OTHER SYSTEMS UP TO 50 PCT MORE EXPENSIVE ARE LISTED ON THE LINE PRINTER.

IF YOU WISH TO CHANGE ANY DESIGN CRITERIA, INDICATE WHICH STATEMENT NUMBER.
IF NOT TYPE 10. DONT FORGET DECIMAL.
    10.

Fig. 8.3 Required performance criteria for an elevator system are
defined on a computer-console typewriter by the architect. The program operates in conventional mode, asking questions through the
typewriter. The architect types in the answers on the same paper.
(The circled numbers are the ones the architect types.) After the computer indicates which system is least expensive, the operator can
modify the design criteria and quickly learn the cost implications.

fundamental to the most cherished human values which cannot be rendered in forms acceptable for computation but cannot be left out of the
design process. If architecture is to continue to express these changing
values, architects must find solutions previously unanticipated.

Therefore, the "black-box" routine can be no more than partially successful. More promising are techniques which engage high speed and
machine precision with the intuitive and random-access capability of the
human mind. This is particularly obvious when we consider that we are

POPULATION = NO ELEV	SPEED	653. CAPACITY	RENTABLE AREA = HC	WT-SEC	98000. RTT	COST	NRSF/ELEV
4	300	2000	0.19	23.	95.	124800.	24500.
4	350	2000	0.20	22.	90.	131800.	24500.
4	350	2500	0.23	24.	99.	143800.	24500.
5	200	2000	0.19	23.	115.	138500	19600.
5	200	2500	0.24	24.	124.	153500.	19600.
5	250	2000	0.22	20.	103.	147250.	19600.
5	250	2500	0.26	22.	112.	162250.	19600.
5	250	3000	0.29	23.	118.	177250.	19600.
5	300	2000	0.24	19.	95.	156000.	19600.
5	300	2500	0.28	20.	104.	171000.	19600.
5	300	3000	0.31	22.	110.	186000.	19600.
5	350	2000	0.25	18.	90.	164750.	19600.
5	350	2500	0.29	19.	99.	179750.	19600.
6	200	2000	0.23	19.	115.	166200.	16333.
6	200	2500	0.28	20.	124.	184200.	16333.
6	250	2000	0.26	17.	103.	176700.	16333.
6	300	2000	0.28	15.	95.	187200.	16333.

TOTAL SOLUTIONS EXPLORED =   270.

Fig. 8.4   Besides listing the least expensive system, the computer also prints out all elevator systems up to 150 percent of the least expensive.

still designing for people. And as long as people react to their environment intuitively, architects cannot subordinate intuitive capabilities to the sequential precision of computer logic. A symbiosis of man and machine is needed, and programs which properly engage the two are required. Only in that way can the subjective abstractions of human values be properly balanced with the objective of the computer.

John Galbraith has put this concept so well that the AIA has quoted him on its membership cards: "We must explicitly assert the claims of beauty against those of economics. That something is cheaper, more convenient or more efficient is no longer decisively in its favor."

A design system based on this bilateral approach is evolving in architectural offices. It attempts to optimize subsystems independently for economy but allows the architect to guide and restrict the design. The program envisions six sections. At this time, several pieces are operational, but some are still "blue sky."

1. *Architectural Systems.* Performance criteria (acoustics, flexibility, etc.) retrieve acceptable systems. Selection of systems determines initial and maintenance costs.

2. *Mechanical Systems.* Performance criteria (control, flexibility, etc.) define alternate systems. Selection of systems determines initial, maintenance, and operational costs.

3. *Structural Systems.* Performance criteria (span, fireproofing, etc.) define acceptable system. Selection of system determines initial cost.

4. *Vertical Circulation.* Design standards and zoning define acceptable solutions and cost.

```
PROGRAM WILL PAUSE FOR PAPER ADJUSTMENT OR DATA SWITCH ADJUSTMENT.
SET DATA SWITCH 15 TO SUPPRESS INSTRUCTIONS.

EARLY START ESTIMATE

*    COPIT    *  LOCATION  * DEVELOPMENT* ESCALATION *
*    1.25     *  .80-1.40  *  .90-1.10   * 1.00-1.10  *
*             *            *             *            *
@    1.25        1.03          1.03          1.05
PROJECT FACTOR =    1.39




PROJECT TITLE AND DATE
TEST 3-22-67

OPERATOR'S NAME
THOMSEN

GROSS HEATED AREA OF BUILDING
10000.

SECTION 1.  ESTIMATE COST OF EXTERIOR WALL SYSTEMS*********************************

ESTIMATE FLOOR TO EXTERIOR WALL RATIO (GROSS AREA PER FLOOR/LIN FT OF EXTERIOR
WALL) - APPROXIMATELY 15. TO 35. IS USUAL FOR A SIMPLE BUILDING.
20.

*                    SYSTEM      *  PCT  *  UNIT COST  *  HEIGHT  *
*                                *       *            *          *
     BRICK W BLK                    85.       3.50         13.
*                                *       *            *          *
     GLASS                          15.       5.00         13.
*                                *       *            *          *

CAULKING ESTIMATED AT .02/SQ FT =     278.48

TOTAL COST OF EXTERIOR WALLS =    33992.71
COST PER SQ FT OF BUILDING AREA =     3.39

TO RECALCULATE THIS SECTION TYPE '1.'.


SECTION 2.  ESTIMATE COST OF ROOF SYSTEMS*****************************************

ESTIMATE FLOOR TO ROOF RATIO  (GROSS BUILDING AREA/ROOF  AREA)
2.
*                    SYSTEM      *  PCT *  UNIT COST  *
*                                *      *            *
     BU IN & FILL                  100       .80
*                                *      *            *

FLASHING ESTIMATED AT .07/SQ FT OF ROOF = 487.35

*            *ESTIMATED TOTAL SQ FT OF SKYLIGHTS
     20.
ESTIMATED SKYLIGHT COST =    250.63

TOTAL COST OF ROOF SYSTEMS =    6077.07
COST PER SQ FT OF BUILDING AREA =    0.60

TO RECALCULATE THIS SECTION TYPE '1.'.
```

Fig. 8.5 A cost estimating for early design stages works as follows:
The operator (architect) drops two cards in the card reader. The program is called off a magnetic disk, and the console typewriter types
the above. As in the other program, COPIT is a factor entered for contractor's overhead, profit, insurance, and taxes. LOCATION anticipates
regional cost changes from national average price data. DEVELOPMENT
includes site contracts, taxes, bidding climate, etc. ESCALATION anticipates price fluctuations from design to bidding time. The designer types
the proper factors under each category for this job (circled), and the
computer computes and prints the project factor, which is used as a
multiplier on the remainder of the building costs. The program continues to estimate the cost of the basic building systems. Above is the
section for exterior walls. The designer inputs the circled information;
the machine does the rest. In addition to exterior wall systems, roof,
floor, ceiling, and partition systems are computed.

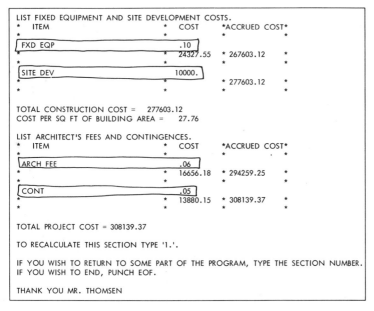

```
LIST FIXED EQUIPMENT AND SITE DEVELOPMENT COSTS.
 *    ITEM                          *   COST     *ACCRUED COST*
 *                                  *            *             *
  ┌ FXD EQP                              .10 ┐
 *                                  24327.55  * 267603.12   *
 *                                  *            *             *
  ┌ SITE DEV                          10000. ┐
 *                                  *          * 277603.12   *
 *                                  *            *             *

TOTAL CONSTRUCTION COST =   277603.12
COST PER SQ FT OF BUILDING AREA =    27.76

LIST ARCHITECT'S FEES AND CONTINGENCES.
 *    ITEM                          *   COST     *ACCRUED COST*
 *                                  *            *       .     *
  ┌ ARCH FEE                            .06 ┐
 *                                  16656.18  * 294259.25   *
 *                                  *            *             *
  ┌ CONT                               .05 ┐
 *                                  13880.15  * 308139.37   *
 *                                  *            *             *

TOTAL PROJECT COST = 308139.37

TO RECALCULATE THIS SECTION TYPE '1.'.

IF YOU WISH TO RETURN TO SOME PART OF THE PROGRAM, TYPE THE SECTION NUMBER.
IF YOU WISH TO END, PUNCH EOF.

THANK YOU MR. THOMSEN
```

Fig. 8.6   Items for fixed equipment, site development, or other special costs may be input either as percentages of the building cost or as lump sums. Finally, total project cost is calculated. At any point in the program, a section may be recalculated to determine savings or cost penalties if any criterion is changed. At the end of the program when the total price is known, it is possible to return to an intermediate location within the program for adjustments.

5. *Operation Economics.* Construction costs, site, fees, etc., define costs. Operational costs and other economic criteria produce expected income.

6. *Building Geometry.* Total building areas and volumes are computed, and income-producing space is compared with total with code restrictions implied.

The program can be set up in such a way that the operator/architect can range from one section to another at will, pursuing both his aesthetic inclinations and the implications of each new bit of information he gleans from the calculations.

Here is how an architect might make it work.

Assume this architect has a client who wants to build a high-quality office building. It will be built in a prestigious area, and while the builder will not be interested in spending money for corporate "image," he realizes that his tenants will expect quality and durability. The land costs are high; so maximum site development is appropriate.

In order to solve this general problem, the architect uses this complex of programs. He might first begin with the geometry routines. He inputs

```
EARLY START ESTIMATE

*   COPIT   * LOCATION   * DEVELOPMENT* ESCALATION *
       1.25        1.06          1.10          1.04
PROJECT FACTOR =    1.51


PROJECT TITLE AND DATE
SKILL CENTER - FLINT, MICHIGAN          11 MAY 1967
SUBMITTED BY
BYRON STENIS

AIA EQUIVALENT AREA
   93122.

GROSS ENCLOSED AREA
    88438.

SECTION 1.  ESTIMATE COST OF EXTERIOR WALL SYSTEMS******************************

ESTIMATE EXTERIOR WALL RATIO (LIN FT OF XWALL/ENCLOSED AREA).
APPROXIMATELY .03-.06 IS USUAL.
    0.0229

*             SYSTEM          * PCT  * UNIT COST * HEIGHT*
FACE BRICK & 8IN CONC BLK-INSUL.   43.40        2.57      7.00
FACE BRICK & 8IN CONC BLK-INSUL.   19.10        2.57     11.00
FACE BRICK & 8IN CONC BLK-INSUL.    3.30        2.57     13.00
FACE BRICK & 8IN CONC BLK-INSUL.    6.10        2.57      4.00
STEEL WINDOW WALL W/CLEAR GLASS    62.50        4.25      2.00
STEEL WINDOW WALL W/CLEAR GLASS    20.90        4.25      9.00
STEEL WINDOW WALL W/CLEAR GLASS     7.30        4.25     11.00
STEEL WINDOW WALL W/WIRE GLASS      6.10        5.70      5.00
METAL FASCIA PANEL 3IN 24GA.       99.10        1.12      5.00
                                    0.00        0.00      0.00
CAULKING ESTIMATED AT .02/SQ FT =   2681.08

EXTERIOR DOORS, HDW.& MISC. WALL   8556.40   130790.70
                TOTAL COST OF EXTERIOR WALL SYSTEMS =    130790.70
                              AIA COST PER SQ FT =           1.40
                            GROSS COST PER SQ FT =           1.47

SECTION 2.  ESTIMATE COST OF ROOF SYSTEMS*******************************************

ESTIMATE FLOOR TO ROOF RATIO (ENCLOSED AREA/TOTAL ROOF AREA)
    1.13
*             SYSTEM          * PCT  * UNIT COST *
BUILT UP ROOF                     100.00       0.19
RIGID ROOF INSULATION 2IN         100.00       0.30
ACOUSTICAL TYPE METAL DECK         43.00       0.65
METAL DECK GALV 20GAGE 11/2 IN     57.00       0.37
5X5 SPECIAL GRID & LAY IN PANEL    14.50       1.08
                                    0.00       0.00
FLASHING AT .07/SQ FT OF ROOF = 8289.57
ROOF CANTS, CURBS & MISC ROOF     11434.87      154370.78
                TOTAL COST OF ROOF SYSTEMS =    154370.78
                           AIA COST PER SQ FT =      1.65
```

Fig. 8.7 The same program will work with card, instead of typewriter input, producing the above output.

core dimensions, overall plan size, and floor-to-floor dimensions, and includes basic code restrictions on maximum height and volume limitations. With the computer's help, he calculates the maximum number of floors, the total net rentable area, and the total gross area.

The next step might be to call the mechanical routine and, based on the net areas and applicable codes, calculate with more precision the core size based on actual toilet-room sizes (fixture ratios from the code would be part of the program), duct spaces, electrical spaces, etc. The decisions are made on the location of mechanical floors, chases, and basic mechanical systems. Outputs are required dimensions, mechanical spaces, and mechanical costs.

At this point he may go back to the geometry program to refine his earlier assumptions on core size and net and gross areas. From there he might then call the structural program, which will output the required depth of structural sections and their costs. After he evaluates this information, he calls the elevator program and sizes vertical circulation. He computes architectural costs and makes a trial run with the economics program computing the investor's return on the investment.

Now, this is the point where the design really begins. The architect has a prototype building designed on common approaches to office buildings. But he is hardly satisfied. The objective is to continue jumping from one program to another following hunches and exploring possibilities.

For instance, he knows that the code's height and volume restrictions limit income-producing space, but if he can squeeze in another floor or two within those restrictions he may help his client.

Using the geometry program and the structural program together, he discovers that, if he goes to a slightly more expensive but shallower floor beam, he can save enough inches in each floor-to-floor dimension to add additional floors. With the economics program he determines that the increased rent from the additional area more than compensates for the slight additional structural cost. Of course, now he must reanalyze the elevators, for while the total vertical travel has not changed, the number of stops has increased. He does so, and finds that slight increases in speed for little additional money solve his problem.

The same comparisons might be made with alternate core arrangements, mechanical systems, elevators, and so forth. While he is working with the elevators, he tries another hunch. He goes to more expensive and faster elevators but saves one cab. The total cost of the elevators is greater, but the cab space is picked up for income-producing space throughout all floors of the building. Again, it more than compensates for the additional cost, and the faster system is selected.

This program is not working now, and it probably will never work in the precise form described. However, 80 percent of the pieces now run in various forms.

Gaps need to be filled in, and the control executive system to coordinate the group of programs must be written. Inevitably, it will be, not only by Caudill Rowlett Scott, but also by many architects across the nation. It is intolerable to try to do a precision job of design with today's antiquated, clumsy arrangement of consultants. The above routines could be done in a few minutes. The same work, if dependent on today's awkward techniques of communication among structural, mechanical, and elevator consultants, cost estimators, economists, land planners, and architects, might never get done.

Another approach to "design systems" is under way at Computer Service, Inc., and Reynolds, Smith and Hills, Architects and Engineers, both of Jacksonville, Florida, who are jointly developing an Architectural Building Design System (ADS). ADS will also provide the design team with a tool to help solve communication problems associated with a mathematical model of the building. A series of computer programs will use these data to provide cost estimates and design information for the civil, mechanical, electrical, and structural disciplines as the design progresses from preliminary concept to final plans and specifications.

ADS is also being developed in a modular-building-block fashion not only to achieve flexibility but also to produce usable computer programs during the development period. The total development effort will span several years and will be highly sensitive to advances in the state of the art of computer technology.

Norman Bryan, President of Computer Service, Inc., feels the main problem areas of ADS fall in the data management and man-machine communications areas. Information systems are complex to design and require highly specialized talent. The amount of "human adaptation" to make the system effective will continue to be a major problem.

8.4   Large-scale Planning

The architectural profession is scrambling to develop techniques to plan and administer large-scale building programs. Techniques applicable to immediate-use, individual buildings are inadequate for clients anticipating building programs which will continue over several years. (Indeed, many have no end in sight and instead expect continued growth indefinitely.) There are a number of essential differences between the one-shot, individual building project and a continuing institutional building program.

First, particularly at colleges and universities, it no longer makes sense to design a complete master plan into which an institution will grow. Continued growth has become a fact of life, with most educational facilities demanding solutions for growth systems rather than static plans. The designer must create a system, an abstraction, rather than a physical representation.

Secondly, detailed function is often ill-defined in large-scale projects.

Many college administrators have recognized that it is impossible for anyone to understand clearly the changing complexities of academic teaching and research, and even worse, time lags in design and construction often make even well-thought-out facilities outdated by the time of occupancy. Similarly, it is useless to query the faculty for this information. Frequently, the present faculty has moved to other campuses by the time construction is complete, or the individual faculty members cannot interpret their views in relation to the overall planning. The only final solution lies in intelligent projections of probable future evolution, with the architecture designed as a flexible common denominator between the present and the future.

Thirdly, one of the most perplexing problems for architects and administrators is the grasp of a basic understanding of activities in nonscheduled campus space such as libraries, student centers, and dormitories. These spaces often constitute up to 90 percent of a campus.

A study for recording existent campus facilities and projecting future needs was completed in December, 1966, at the University of Wisconsin. John Yurkovich, the principal investigator, has explained that research included a number of space-management techniques that surely have almost universal contemporary importance for large planning projects. As part of his research project, Yurkovich developed, tested, and implemented on the University of Wisconsin campus at Madison an outstanding space-accounting system. It contains the following key features:

1. *A Space-classification System.* All spaces on campus are recorded, not only as total square feet, but for quality, performance, and appropriate uses. From the data it is possible to predict alternate academic uses of the space.

2. *A Perpetual Space Inventory.* The proper management techniques within the university administration system were developed to maintain the space-classification system. Necessary computer programs were developed to update the data bank with new information.

3. *A Room-utilization Study.* A set of computer programs was developed to measure some aspects of the space use on campus. Items such as classroom and student-station utilization were measured. Wisconsin administrators now have a routine device to measure the effectiveness of some of their existing buildings.

4. *A System for Projecting Future Student Enrollment and Staff Needs.* This includes internal growth trends, policies for growth, and external influences to project future campus population.

5. *A System for Projecting Requirements for Future Physical Facilities.* This was developed with the three basic building blocks of (a) existing space, (b) existing utilization, and (c) future population.

John Yurkovich's excellent project provided many of the fundamental concepts of a simulation research project at Duke University. This is an Educational Facilities Laboratories supported research project. Duke University, in collaboration with Hews, Holz and Willard and Caudill Rowlett Scott, is developing a computer-aided study to give planners a powerful tool in their design efforts. Robert Mattox, Project Manager for Caudill Rowlett Scott, describes the project as follows:

First, we simply wish to provide more accurate information on a routine basis to the planning team. Computer techniques are being developed to help planners organize the large quantities of data unique to campus planning. Then computer modeling techniques will demonstrate the implication of alternate solutions to detailed problems before one solution is chosen.

Computer techniques will be developed to provide an economical means to update this planning information for a continuous planning system rather than a static "master plan."

Furthermore, methods for collecting and recording more meaningful data are being developed to gain a better insight into the planning influences of "nonscheduled" activities in such facilities as libraries, dormitories, and student unions.

The business of planning with a computer has caused much soul searching and questioning. As usual, when automation is brought in, it becomes necessary to understand the human process far better than before. In order to find the right way to engage the computer, the planning process has been clearly structured and defined as follows:

1. *Allocation.* Analyzing needs and estimating space requirements to meet those needs

2. *Location.* Assigning existing space to activities and siting new construction

3. *Evaluation.* Weighing alternate solutions before selecting a plan

Programs are being written in all these phases, and some of the knots in campus planning are coming untied, but it has not been without difficulty.

For instance, our early concepts were aimed at increasing the efficiency of academic teaching space. We analyzed classroom utilization, searching for improved standards, compared room capacities with frequency of use, and studied ways of increasing utilization through more efficient computer-implemented scheduling techniques.

Only after we were well into the project did we realize that we were nibbling at the edges of the problem. Eighty-five to ninety percent of the campus's physical facilities were nonscheduled (dormitories, libraries, research space, student centers, etc.). If we made a breakthrough and increased the efficiency of the scheduled classroom space by 20 percent, we would affect the total efficiency only 2 or 3 percent.

While rather sophisticated techniques were being refined for measuring classroom utilization, no one had gone very far in measuring all the other kinds of space used. Indeed, the terms for measuring them seem difficult to find. (One can say the student seat in a classroom is used 80 percent of the available class hours, but how do you measure the effectiveness of a library, or the lounge in a dormitory?)

The study shifted gears, and concentration was placed on measuring nonscheduled activities. Large groups of students kept diaries, and their diverse activities were punched on cards and graphed.

During this work, a simulation program was conceived which would contain the following:

1. Project activities (the function, activities, and programs of the university, such as courses of study, football, seminars, administrative work, maintenance programs)

2. Geographic locations of facilities (a coordinate grid with the locations of all campus space noted)

3. Affinities (the functional relationships expressed as relative attractions or repulsion between activities)

4. Desired space utilization (maximum capacity for all facilities for each kind of activity)

5. Cost projections (including escalation figures for future construction of all building types as well as conversion costs

6. Construction dollars available (a list of funds usable for construction with the probable interest rates so that use of funds one year could be compared with the use of the same funds in another year)

The current status of the project is this. Emphasis is being put on measuring student activity and using it as a gauge to measure existing facilities with an emphasis on the "evaluation" aspect of the study. Indeed a rather large program—which has been called an "evaluator" instead of a simulator, has been constructed and continues to grow.

The evaluation part of the program has received much attention. The evaluation program will be developed in three levels, moving from basic input-output-reporting procedures to simulating portions of the campus life. In this program, the physical aspects of a campus are described as space and its functions as activities. As activities grow, demand for space increases, and actions are required to keep the system in balance. A planner seeks the best combination of actions to solve the problems of a changing campus. The evaluation program is designed to help him choose the best—almost like the computer-implemented war games developed to teach military strategy.

One of the old saws among computer aficionados is that one always overestimates what can be accomplished in the near future but underestimates the opportunities of the next decade.

This is particularly true in architecture. Even if the profession remained as it is today, computers would be useful in many ways. At Caudill Rowlett Scott, every department has found useful applications. In only two years over a hundred programs have been written, a computer has been leased which is now running overtime, and many staff members have developed the attitude that the machine is indispensable.

But of course architecture will not stay as it is today. Firms will become larger and increasingly more specialized. Today's urban problems will increase. Architectural, mechanical, and electrical systems will compound their sophistication, and the complexities of economics as a design determinant will confound architects equipped with only today's tools.

No longer will architects be able to squander young talent by convincing well-educated graduates that they should work at low pay drafting door details as a prerequisite "internship."

Computers alone will not mitigate all architecture's contemporary ills, but they will surely help architects face the future's increasing complexities with more assurance and skill. And assuming that architecture continues to attract intelligent, energetic youth and equip them with technology's newest and most effective tools, it just may succeed in hammering tomorrow's megalopolis into a viable environment.

CHAPTER NINE *Research in*

Computer Applications

to Architecture

By Lavette C. Teague, Jr., AIA

Given the magnitude of some of the total architectural problems described in the previous chapter, it seems natural that some active research should be centered on these problem areas. The systematic collection and manipulation of data from a number of building subsystems is by no means a trivial problem and is likely to require considerable time and effort to solve. An initial step toward the solution of these systems problems is described in this chapter.

Mr. Teague is an instructor in the Department of Civil Engineering at M.I.T., where he completed his Ph.D. in systems in 1968. He received his B. Arch. from M.I.T. in 1957, and M.S. in Civil Engineering in 1965. A registered architect, he has a varied background of architectural experience, including work with firms such as Synergetics in North Carolina and the Rust Engineering Company, Birmingham. In 1964, he was awarded the Certificate of the National Council of Architectural Registration Boards; and in 1966, he won the Brunner scholarship from the New York AIA for research in architecture.

9.1 Introduction

Current uses of the computer in architectural practice were described in the preceding chapter. This chapter discusses areas of research in computer-aided architectural design, with emphasis on recent work at M.I.T. The concluding section discusses the computer in relation to changing professional practice.

As will be evident from the historical notes that follow, many architects recognized the potential of computers as design aids as quickly as their engineering colleagues. Yet the application of computers in engineering practice, particularly in structural, highway, and air-conditioning system design, is further advanced than in most architectural offices.

There are two principal reasons for this state of affairs. First, the engineering disciplines already possessed technical theories on which their analysis and design methods were based. These design procedures were themselves well-defined and widely accepted as the basis of professional practice. No commonly held theoretical and analytical base existed in architecture, nor were there correspondingly well-defined design procedures. Second, the problems and responsibilities of the architect have been more complex. In his usual role as coordinator of the building-design team, the architect has had to ensure the compatibility of all the constituent building subsystems and the unification of all the contributing design disciplines. This responsibility implies a broad concern with the interactive and integrative aspects of design as well as attention to a wide range of value judgments and associated design criteria. The total problem in the eye of the architect is likely to be more complex than the sum of the parts as seen by each consultant in his own area of expertise. In addition, the architect must relate the requirements and interests of the client, explicit and implied, to the experience and values of the design professions.

Thus further research is needed before the architect can expect a computer to assist greatly in the problems of everyday practice. The major areas of the required research are related to the two historical reasons just cited for the lack of wide current use of computers by architects. In the first place, theoretical bases for architectural analysis and design need to be developed. These theories must not only be concerned with particular methods for analysis of buildings and evaluation or prediction of their performance; they should also lead to a better understanding of systems of complex relationships. Techniques for analysis and evaluation originating in other fields can undoubtedly be transferred to architecture, but the adaptation to the architectural context has to be made. In the second place, the computer must facilitate the unification and integration of the building-design process as well as of the building which is the final product of that process. The computer must become a useful means of communication among all the people who make design decisions.[18,28] The hardware and programming problems associated with accomplishing this kind of communication and integration are not trivial. They are themselves the object of considerable current research and development, and they continue to generate new problems. Many of these problems become apparent only as successful solutions are achieved to previously perceived problems. Moreover, the need of the architect to deal with the design as a whole suggests that a certain critical scale, a minimum capability in scope and complexity, is necessary before the computer can provide significant effectiveness in general practice.

On the one hand, the application of information-processing technology to building design requires major advances in design theory; on the other hand, it makes the new research possible. The computer has given the architect a new focus for research—design theory and its applications in design technology. The computer raises new kinds of questions about architectural analysis and at the same time provides a way of obtaining meaningful answers.

Clark and Souder saw this research as leading to a new science of architecture, which they distinguished from the art of architecture.[3]

> Let us not use the word *architecture* . . . to suggest at the same time an intellectual process, a material object and an emotional experience . . . we can talk of the *art* (or craft, or technology) of architecture as the immediate practical process of creating new examples, and of the more remote *science* of architecture as the process of inquiry into relationships and the development of theories about these relationships.

Thus a science of architecture will concentrate on architectural relationships, on interactions, on interfaces and conflicts. Such a theory of architecture will be particularly concerned with spatial relationships and with the way in which various building systems affect each other. It will help relate the building to the performance standards and criteria to which it is designed. As this science develops, it will yield general theories which practitioners of the art of architecture can apply to particular design problems.

Even a simple building is a complex of systems with thousands of variables subject to the decision of the architect. The potential number of combinations is immense. Thus both the development and testing of the theories of a science of architecture as well as their application in practice are dependent on the use of computers. They imply a design technology which uses the computer as a design medium.[2,12]

To assist the designer effectively, it is not enough for the computer simply to store and record design data and decisions. It must also retain and manipulate the ways in which the data are related and the decisions interact. The ability of the designer to deal in more realistic detail with the complexities of building relationships should lead to a greater understanding of design problems and perhaps to solutions more suited to their social purpose.

From these general concepts follow the major issues and areas of current research. Among them are questions of theory, implementation, and application to practice. Study of the theoretical aspects of building design involves analysis of design information and methods of predicting, simulating, and evaluating building performance. It leads to problems of design synthesis and optimization. Implementation of these theoretical concepts in a computer system raises questions related to man-machine communication, computer graphics, computer representation of relational data complexes, program compatibility, and data transfer between programming systems. The application of computers to architectural problems in education and practice is concerned not only with special-purpose hardware, remote computing, and time sharing but also with design methods and even the psychology of interactive computer-aided design.

9.2   Historical Notes

The beginning of research in the application of computers to architectural problems coincides roughly with the introduction of the second generation of digital computers about 1960. As early as 1961, students at M.I.T. had investigated the problem of assigning activities to the various spaces of a building and had formulated a simplified version of the problem in terms of a linear-programming model so as to minimize travel distances among the spaces. By December, 1964, when the Boston Architectural Center sponsored a conference on "Architecture and the Computer,"[31] research results had already been reported, with much of the work originating in Cambridge.

Work by Miller, Roos, Fenves, Logcher, and others[9,10,17,22] had approached the use of the computer as a practical aid to the design engineer in related fields of civil engineering. The SKETCHPAD system by Sutherland and its subsequent development[4,14,27] had pointed the way toward graphical communication between men and computers. Experimental time-sharing systems[5,8] were in operation to demonstrate that a number of people could work jointly on a common problem, each at his own console.

No attempt will be made to give even a survey of architectural research in the computer field. Instead, a few noteworthy accomplishments will be mentioned. In the United States, they may be represented by the work of Alexander and that of Souder and Clark.

Alexander's *Notes on the Synthesis of Form*[1] presents basic concepts for the development of rational design procedures and for the formulation of associated theories of what was described above as a "science of architecture." These ideas include the necessity of stating explicitly the requirements which the design is to fulfill and the importance of seeing which requirements are determinants of architectural, physical form. Alexander's approach gives particular attention to the interactions among the design requirements. It emphasizes the relational aspects of design and recognizes the fact that information about relationships often provides the most important data with which the designer deals.

In spite of the shortcomings of the specific method proposed by Alexander, many of which he has since recognized, the basic attitude expressed in his book toward the use of computers in architecture remains valid. His work illustrates the kind of careful analysis of design tasks that is a prerequisite to effective use of the computer. It demonstrates that most architectural problems have so many design requirements and such complex patterns of relationships among them that these relationships must be explicitly represented by some abstract algebraic structure. If, in addition, this algebraic structure is itself represented in a computer, then the computer can be used to help exhibit the structure of the problem to the designer and to show him the consequences of the decisions he made in selecting the list of requirements and in analyzing their interactions.

While Alexander's work concentrated at the early or conceptual stage of the design, to help the architect in his search for a form appropriate to the problem requirements, the work of Souder and Clark[26] focused on a later stage in the process. It was more concerned with the description and evaluation of the proposed design.

The particular building type studied by Souder and Clark was a hospital. Their approach was of greater generality, however. A principal contribution of their work was the development of computer programs which demonstrated in the architectural context the technical feasibility of modeling the plan of a building using a light pen and a cathode-ray tube to provide graphical input and output. In addition, because of its particular importance in hospital planning, they studied the circulation system, or "commerce" system as they called it, of the hospital in considerable detail. They used statistical techniques to simulate and thereby evaluate the performance of alternative designs. Others have also used simulation techniques in hospital-planning studies and in airport-terminal design as well. Recent work by Clark has continued the early emphasis on building description and evaluation.[34]

In Britain, parallel work was being done. There was a similar interest in problems of space allocation and synthesis of building geometry. There were both theoretical and application studies, using both deterministic and heuristic approaches.[20,30,32] A demonstration computer program was developed by Fair, Flowerdew, Munro, and Rowley to permit the modular planning of buildings using a system of standard prefabricated commercial components.[7] Checking the plans against criteria for adequate structure, illumination, ventilation, and floor area was one of the features of the programs. Newman revised and extended these programs to incorporate cathode-ray-tube input and output.[21]

9.3   BUILD—Prototype of an Information System for Building Design

While the word "computer" is a compact and widely used name, the less convenient term "information-processing system" is a more accurate description of the machine. It permits the storage of information and the transformation of information from one pattern or arrangement to another.

To use the computer in the design of buildings, it is necessary to identify the relevant information which is to be stored in the computer and the operations which must be performed to carry out useful transformations of the information so that the results will be meaningful to the designer. Thus there must be a means of representing design information in the machine and a means of communication between the designer and the computer so that he can enter information, specify the transformations to be carried out, and obtain and interpret the results.

The problem of identifying the information used by the architect as well as the operations he performs upon it as a part of the building-design process is a problem of analysis. This analysis asks the same kinds of questions as those which lead to the science of architecture mentioned above, and thus is closely related to it.

The problem of providing man-machine communication is more a problem of design—of developing a suitable mode of interaction between an architect and a computer system which he will use as a design medium to represent and transform the solution to a building-design problem.

BUILD, a pilot version of an information system for building design, has recently been developed at M.I.T. as an aid to research. How the BUILD research has approached the problems of architectural systems analysis including the representation of design information and of man-machine communication, especially the aspects of computer-system design related to interactive problem solving, is discussed below.

A study, "Systems Analysis in Building Design," conducted cooperatively by the Departments of Architecture and Civil Engineering at M.I.T. under a grant from the National Science Foundation provided the theoretical basis for BUILD. The preliminary analysis led to a general categorization of information used in architectural design decisions as well as to an investigation of the information requirements for specific design decisions and the transformations of information associated with the corresponding design operations. The major groupings of design information were design objectives, performance standards, performance measurements, and the description of the building being designed as a physical object with its constituent systems.[6]

The initial work on BUILD has focused on the information and the operations required to describe a building, with particular emphasis on geometry and spatial relationships. It has dealt with four of the building systems identified in the systems-analysis study—activities, spaces, surfaces, and structure, as indicated in the example of the following section.

The computer-system capabilities which facilitate communication and interaction between the designer and the internal representation of his problem are provided for BUILD by its operating framework—the Integrated Civil Engineering System. ICES, as the name implies, is intended to integrate procedures of computer-aided problem solving from many different fields of civil engineering, allowing diverse disciplines and approaches to be applied to a single problem.[23] However, the ICES concepts and facilities are not inherently limited to the context of civil engineering; they should prove useful when applied to many other tasks in the area of building design.

Among the many features of the ICES approach, it will be sufficient to mention here those which are most important to the user of the computer as a design aid.

The first of these is the concept of a command-structured problem-oriented language. Such a language consists of words and phrases from the familiar technical vocabulary of the user. These words and phrases are organized into commands. Each command instructs the computer to perform specific operations. In general, the commands, which correspond to transformations of information by the computer and which signify analysis and design processes or parts of processes to the user, may be executed in any sequence the user prescribes. This freedom of sequence for design procedures is, of course, subject to the logical limitation that the information necessary for the performance of a process must be available to the computer at the time when the process is to be executed. The modular organization of programs and processes associated with the commands of such a language facilitates the modification of the language to accommodate the user and encourages the incremental evolution of increasingly effective design procedures. The resulting flexibility has been particularly suited to the kind of experimentation and research involved in the development of BUILD. The next section contains an example of the command-structured problem-oriented language for BUILD.

Within ICES each problem area has its own problem-oriented language. All these languages invoke computer programs which have been organized to increase the ease with which all the available problem-solving capabilities can be directed toward a single problem. This means, for example, that the procedures of the Structural Design Language, many of them widely used by structural engineers, can soon be applied to the description of the structure provided in BUILD.

ICES also encompasses a variety of modes of communication between the user and the computer, including cards, remote typewriter, plotters, printers, and cathode-ray-tube displays with light-pen input. How to combine these various means of interaction effectively is itself an important area of investigation.

Finally, the ability to define and operate on relational data structures in ICES[15] is important in providing design aids to the architect—for whom information about relationships can be the most critical information in the design process.

The current scope and capabilities of BUILD are presented in terms of an example. It should be emphasized that the computer programs constituting BUILD are not restricted to the solution of this specific example. Any operations defined by BUILD commands can be performed on any building that can be described in the BUILD language. Thus BUILD provides a general capability for executing well-defined procedures requiring specific information. In using these procedures, the designer applies them to a particular building. The ability to define design procedures and their specific information requirements, yet without reference to any particular building, is a key to progress in the development of the basic architectural theory on which more effective use of the computer's design potential depends.

9.4 Example

The following example illustrates typical features of BUILD. The commands for a BUILD program describing a small office building appear in

Fig. 9.1. The commands contained there constitute the computer input as it might be punched into cards or typed in at a remote console by a designer. The commentary which follows discusses the example line by line and should be read in conjunction with the problem statements and the illustrations (Figs. 9.1 to 9.10). Figure 9.1 shows input only. Line numbers are prefixed for purposes of reference; they are not a part of the BUILD input. The commands are written in full for clarity. A regular user of the language can reduce the amount of input by employing an abbreviated form.

```
(1)     BUILD
(2)     BUILDING 'OFFICE EXAMPLE'
(3)     ACTIVITIES
(4)        'DISPLAY'
(5)        'STAIR 1'
(6)        'STAIR 2'
(7)        'SERVICES'
(8)        'SALES'
(9)        'CLERICAL'
(10)       'OFFICES'
(11)       'EXECUTIVE'
(12)       'LOBBY'
(13)    SPACES
(14)       'RM 101' L 96.  W 32. H 20.
(15)       'UPPER FLR' L  96. W 96. H 10.
(16)       'LOWER FLR' L  96. W 96. H 10.
(17)       'RM 102' L 8.  W 16.  H 20.
(18)       'RM 103' L 16.  W 8.  H 20.
(19)    LOCATE SPACE 'RM 101' 20.  30.
(20)    ATTACH
(21)       'LOWER FLR' TO 'RM 101' AT NORTH
(22)       'RM 102' TO 'LOWER FLR' AT EAST Y 12.
(23)       'RM 103' TO 'LOWER FLR' AT WEST Y 72.
(24)       'UPPER FLR' TO 'RM 101' AT NORTH Z 10.
(25)       'UPPER FLR' TO 'LOWER FLR' AT CEILING
(26)       'UPPER FLR' TO 'RM 102' AT WEST Y -12.  Z -10.
(27)       'UPPER FLR' TO 'RM 103' AT EAST Y -72.  Z -10.
(28)    DIVIDE 'RM 101'
(29)       INTERVALS 3 X EQUAL
(30)       NAMES 'BAY 1'  'BAY 2'  'BAY 3'
(31)       END
(32)    DIVIDE 'LOWER FLR'
(33)       INTERVALS 3 X EQUAL
(34)       INTERVALS 3 Y EQUAL
(35)       NAMES 'BAY 4'  'BAY 5'  'BAY 6'  'BAY 7'  'BAY 8'
(36)         'BAY 9'  'BAY 10'  'BAY 11'  'BAY 12'
(37)       END
(38)    DIVIDE 'UPPER FLR'
(39)       INTERVALS 3 X EQUAL
(40)       INTERVALS 3 Y EQUAL
(41)       NAMES 'BAY 21'  'BAY 22'  'BAY 23'  'BAY 24'  'COURT'
(42)         'BAY 26'  'BAY 27'  'BAY 28'  'BAY 29'
(43)       END
(44)    FRAME
```

```
(45)    'BAY 1' WITH SUPPORTS
(46)    'BAY 2' BEAMS
(47)    'BAY 3' WITH SUPPORTS
(48)    'BAY 4' BEAMS
(49)    'BAY 5' BEAMS
(50)    'BAY 6' BEAMS
(51)    'BAY 7' WITH SUPPORTS
(52)    'BAY 9' WITH SUPPORTS
(53)    'BAY 10' WITH SUPPORTS
(54)    'BAY 11' BEAMS
(55)    'BAY 12' WITH SUPPORTS
(56)    'BAY 21'
(57)    'BAY 22' BEAMS
(58)    'BAY 23'
(59)    'BAY 24' BEAMS
(60)    'BAY 26' BEAMS
(61)    'BAY 27'
(62)    'BAY 28' BEAMS
(63)    'BAY 29'
(64)    DIVIDE 'BAY 4'
(65)        INTERVALS 2 X 20.  12.
(66)        NAMES 'RM 104'  'RM 105'
(67)        END
(68)    DIVIDE 'BAY 6'
(69)        INTERVALS 2 X 12.  20.
(70)        NAMES 'RM 106'  'RM 107'
(71)        END
(72)    DIVIDE 'BAY 21'
(73)        INTERVALS 2 X 20.  12.
(74)        NAMES 'RM 201'  'RM 202'
(75)        END
(76)    DIVIDE 'BAY 23'
(77)        INTERVALS 2 X  12.  20.
(78)        NAMES 'RM 203'  'RM 204'
(79)        END
(80)    DIVIDE 'BAY 24'
(81)        INTERVALS 2 X 20.  12.
(82)        NAMES 'RM 205'  'W COURT'
(83)        END
(84)    DIVIDE 'BAY 26'
(85)        INTERVALS 2 X 12.  20.
(86)        NAMES 'E COURT'  'RM 206'
(87)    FRAME
(88)        'RM 205' BEAMS
(89)        'RM 206' BEAMS
(90)    ASSIGN ACTIVITY TO SPACE
(91)        'DISPLAY' TO 'RM 101'
(92)        'STAIR' TO 'RM 102'
(93)        'STAIR' TO 'RM 103'
(94)        'LOUNGE' TO 'RM 104'
(95)        'SERVICE' TO 'RM 105'
(96)        'SERVICE' TO 'BAY 5'
(97)        'SERVICE' TO 'RM 106'
(98)        'LOBBY' TO 'RM 107'
(99)        'SALES' TO 'BAY 7'
(100)       'SALES' TO 'BAY 8'
(101)       'SALES' TO 'BAY 9'
(102)       'CLERICAL' TO 'BAY 10'
(103)       'CLERICAL' TO 'BAY 11'
```

```
(104)   'CLERICAL' TO 'BAY 12'
(105)   'OFFICE' TO 'RM 201'
(106)   'SERVICE' TO 'RM 202'
(107)   'SERVICE' TO 'BAY 22'
(108)   'SERVICE' TO 'RM 203'
(109)   'OFFICE TO 'RM 204'
(110)   'EXECUTIVE' TO 'RM 205'
(111)   'EXECUTIVE' TO 'RM 206'
(112)   'OFFICE' TO 'BAY 25'
(113)   'OFFICE' TO 'BAY 26'
(114)   'OFFICE' TO 'BAY 27'
(115)   ENCLOSE ALL
(116)   TAKEOFF TOTAL VOLUME OF SPACES
(117)   TAKEOFF AREA OF SURFACES
(118)     'W COURT' S WALL
(119)     'COURT' S WALL
(120)     'E COURT' S WALL
(121)   TOTAL
(122)   MATERIALS
(123)     'GLASS' DENSITY 8.  COST 1.75
(124)     'CONCRETE' D 100.  C 2.00
(125)     'ROOF'       D   8.  C 1.10
(126)     'OPEN'        D   0.  C 0.
(127)   SPECIFY MATERIALS FOR SURFACES
(128)     E, S OF 'RM 101' MATERIAL 'GLASS'
(129)     W OF 'RM 101' MATERIAL 'CONCRETE'
(130)     WALLS OF 'RM 102' MATERIAL 'CONCRETE'
(131)     WALLS OF 'RM 103' MATERIAL 'CONCRETE'
(132)     N, W OF 'LOWER FLR' MATERIAL 'GLASS'
(133)     E OF 'BAY 9' MATERIAL 'CONCRETE'
(134)     E OF 'BAY 12' MATERIAL 'CONCRETE'
(135)     W OF 'RM 104' MATERIAL 'CONCRETE'
(136)     N, S OF 'RM 104' MATERIAL 'OPEN'
(137)     WALLS OF 'RM 105' MATERIAL 'CONCRETE'
(138)     WALLS OF 'BAY 5' MATERIAL 'CONCRETE'
(139)     WALLS OF 'RM 106' MATERIAL 'CONCRETE'
(140)     N, S OF 'RM 107' MATERIAL 'OPEN'
(141)     E OF 'RM 107' MATERIAL 'GLASS'
(142)     E, W OF 'UPPER FLR' MATERIAL 'CONCRETE'
(143)     N OF 'UPPER FLR' MATERIAL 'GLASS'
(144)     N, S OF 'RM 201' MATERIAL 'GLASS'
(145)     WALLS OF 'RM 202' MATERIAL 'CONCRETE'
(146)     WALLS OF 'BAY 22' MATERIAL 'CONCRETE'
(147)     WALLS OF 'RM 203' MATERIAL 'CONCRETE'
(148)     N, S OF 'RM 204' MATERIAL 'GLASS'
(149)     E OF 'RM 205' MATERIAL 'GLASS'
(150)     W OF 'RM 206' MATERIAL 'GLASS'
(151)     S OF 'BAY 27' MATERIAL 'GLASS'
(152)     S OF 'BAY 28' MATERIAL 'GLASS'
(153)     S OF 'BAY 29' MATERIAL 'GLASS'
(154)   FLOORS OF ALL MATERIAL 'CONCRETE'
(155)   CEILING OF 'RM 101' MATERIAL 'ROOF'
(156)   CEILING OF 'RM 102' MATERIAL 'ROOF'
(157)   CEILING OF 'RM 103' MATERIAL 'ROOF'
(158)   CEILING OF 'BAY 21' MATERIAL 'ROOF'
(159)   CEILING OF 'BAY 22' MATERIAL 'ROOF'
(160)   CEILING OF 'BAY 23' MATERIAL 'ROOF'
(161)   CEILING OF 'RM 205' MATERIAL 'ROOF'
(162)   CEILING OF 'W COURT' MATERIAL 'OPEN'
```

(163)   CEILING OF 'COURT' MATERIAL 'OPEN'
(164)   CEILING OF 'E COURT' MATERIAL 'OPEN'
(165)   CEILING OF 'RM 206' MATERIAL 'ROOF'
(166)   CEILING OF 'BAY 27' MATERIAL 'ROOF'
(167)   CEILING OF 'BAY 28' MATERIAL 'ROOF'
(168)   CEILING OF 'BAY 29' MATERIAL 'ROOF'
(169)   TAKEOFF WEIGHT OF W WALL 'RM 101'
(170)   PRINT SPACES ASSIGNED TO ACTIVITY 'OFFICE'

Fig. 9.1   Example problem statements

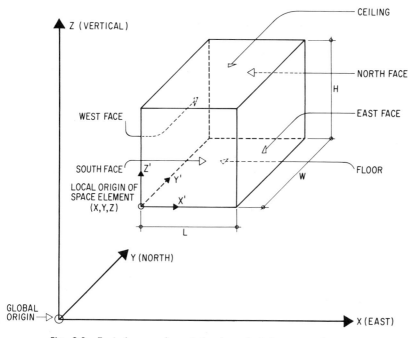

Fig. 9.2   Typical space element showing orientation convention

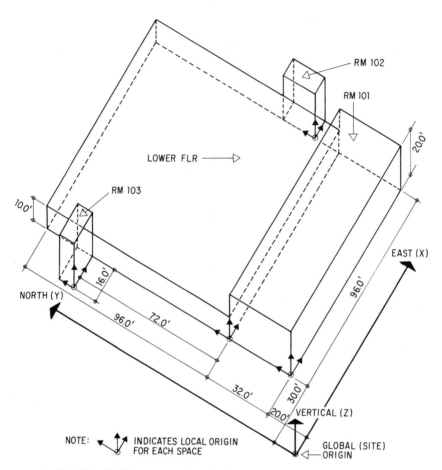

Fig. 9.3 Building spaces after the location of RM 101 and the attachment of RM 102, RM 103, and LOWER FLR

Some of the commands, such as PRINT and TAKEOFF, are requests for output from the computer. These commands and the computer's response are shown separately in Figs. 9.8 and 9.10. The numbered lines correspond to those in Fig. 9.1; the lettered lines are the computer's response.

Considerable simplification has been introduced to reduce the number of statements required for the description. The planning is schematic; the smallest subdivision of space is approximately half a bay.

The command BUILD (line 1) informs the ICES command-processing programs that the commands to follow are in the BUILD language. The word BUILDING (line 2) causes the computer to prepare for a new problem and to store OFFICE EXAMPLE as the problem title. Lines 3 to 12 define the

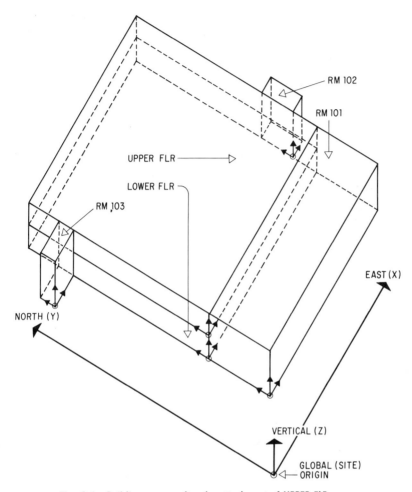

RM 102

RM 101

UPPER FLR ⟶ ▷

LOWER FLR

RM 103

EAST (X)

NORTH (Y)

VERTICAL (Z)

GLOBAL (SITE)
ORIGIN

Fig. 9.4   Building spaces after the attachment of UPPER FLR

ACTIVITIES which the building is to house. Lines 13 to 18 define the principal SPACES of the building, each a rectangular element with the given dimensions. (The orientation convention is as indicated in Fig. 9.2.) At this point in the program, the individual activities and individual spaces exist as isolated and independent entities. No relationships have been defined among them or between them and the site.

The LOCATE command (line 19) relates the two-story space RM 101 to the site. The southwest bottom corner of the space is located 20 feet east and 30 feet north of the southwest corner of the site and at the same level vertically. The edges of the space are parallel to the coordinate axes for the site as shown in Fig. 9.2.

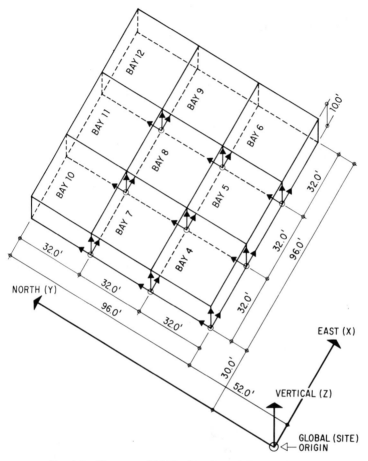

Fig. 9.5   The space LOWER FLR after subdivision by the DIVIDE command

The relationships among these five spaces are established in lines 20 to 27 using the ATTACH command. Line 21 defines the south face of LOWER FLR as adjacent to and coincident with the north face of RM 101.

Because RM 101 has already been located on the site, the location of LOWER FLR on the site is implied. All these relationships are recorded in the computer. In line 22, the west face of RM 102 is a different size from the east face of LOWER FLR. The orientation of each face is fixed, in accordance with the convention illustrated in Fig. 9.2. Therefore, the relative positions of the two spaces can be specified if the location of a single point is given. That point, by convention, is the projection of the origin of RM 102 onto the east face of LOWER FLR. Its y coordinate with respect to the origin of LOWER FLR is 12, as indicated in line 22.

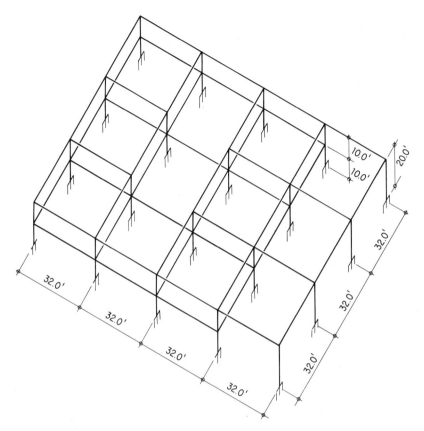

Fig. 9.6 Structure generated by the FRAME command

The building configuration as defined through line 23 is shown in Fig. 9.3. Finally, the UPPER FLR is attached to the other four spaces (lines 24 to 27 and Fig. 9.4).

The remaining spatial relationships are established by successive subdivision of the spaces already defined. For example, the DIVIDE command in lines 28 to 31 causes RM 101 to be subdivided by planes perpendicular to the x axis. These planes cut the x axis into three equal INTERVALS (line 29) and thus divide RM 101 into three equal spaces. A name is given to each of these spaces in line 30; the END statement terminates the DIVIDE command. The effect of the DIVIDE command in lines 32 to 37 is to split LOWER FLR into nine spaces, with three subdivisions in the x direction and three in the y direction. The result of the division of LOWER FLR is shown in Fig. 9.5. A similar subdivision of UPPER FLR is performed in lines 38 to 43.

These commands have subdivided the five original spaces into 32-foot-square bays which will correspond to the main structural frame.

The FRAME command (lines 44 to 63) generates structural members at each space named, columns at the vertical edges and beams at the horizontal edges in the ceiling plane. The words WITH SUPPORTS (line 45) designate that support joints occur at the bottom of the columns of the specified space. Where the word BEAMS occurs, as in line 46, only the horizontal members at the ceiling plane are generated. The resulting structure is shown in Fig. 9.6. JOINT COORDINATE and MEMBER INCIDENCE statements describing this structure in the Structural Design Language are generated by the FRAME command.

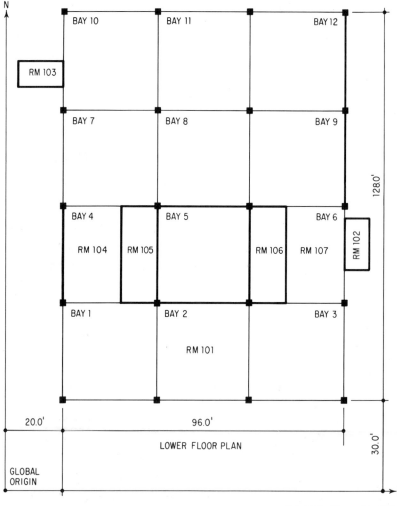

Fig. 9.7 Plan of building

Further subdivision of the structural bays is accomplished in lines 64 to 86. Corresponding plans of the building appear in Fig. 9.7. To simplify the example, a more detailed division of the space into corridors and individual offices is omitted.

A second FRAME command (lines 87 to 89) adds roof beams at the east and west ends of the second-floor courtyard.

Lines 90 to 114 define a relationship between each activity and the corresponding space. In this example, some of the activities occur in more than one space. In other buildings, several activities might occupy the same space.

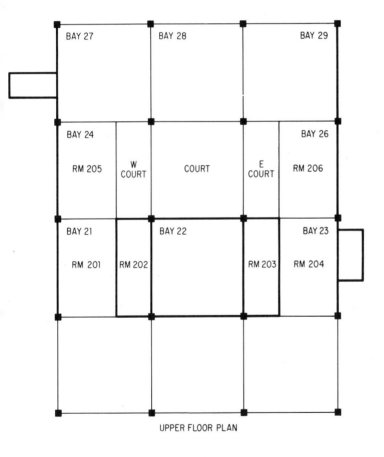

UPPER FLOOR PLAN

after the sequence of DIVIDE commands

```
(116)      TAKEOFF TOTAL VOLUME OF SPACES
 (a)                     12288.00
(117)      TAKEOFF AREA OF SURFACES
(118)            'W COURT' S WALL
 (b)                   120.00
(119)            'COURT' S WALL
 (c)                   320.00
(120)            'E COURT' S WALL
 (d)                   120.00
(121)      TOTAL
 (e)                   560.00
```

Fig. 9.8 Output from TAKEOFF commands. Note: Input lines are numbered to correspond to those of Fig. 9.1. Output lines are identified with letters.

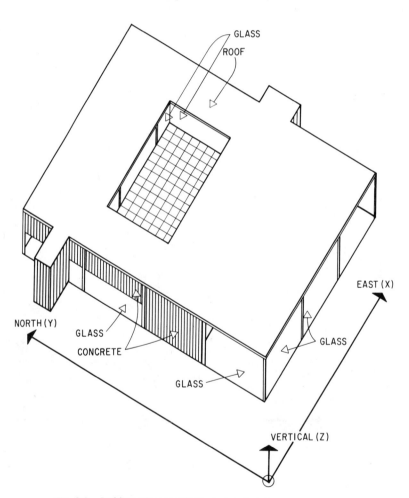

Fig. 9.9 Building after specification of materials

```
(170)    PRINT SPACES ASSIGNED TO ACTIVITY 'OFFICE'
 (f)            RM 201
 (g)            RM 204
 (h)            BAY 25
 (i)            BAY 26
 (j)            BAY 27
```

Fig. 9.10 Output from typical PRINT command. Note: Input lines are numbered to correspond to those of Fig. 9.1. Output lines are identified with letters.

Thus far, the building has been described only as a set of related spaces and an associated structural frame. The physical boundaries or delimiting elements of the spaces make up the system of surfaces. Surfaces (four walls, a floor, and a ceiling) are generated by the ENCLOSE ALL command (line 115) at the faces of all the spaces. However, because of the adjacencies defined by the ATTACH and DIVIDE commands, some of the surfaces are common to two or more spaces. For example, the west wall of the stair RM 102 is the same as the east wall of BAY 4 on the lower floor and BAY 23 on the upper floor. Only one surface is created there, and its relationship to each of the adjacent spaces is recorded.

Now that the surfaces have been defined by their dimensions, enough information is available to permit the designer to obtain takeoffs of areas and volumes, either summarized, as in line 116, or itemized and subtotaled, as in lines 117 to 121. Immediately after reading each TAKEOFF command, the computer prints the desired quantities (see Fig. 9.8). To give the surfaces physical reality, the designer must select materials. Lines 122 to 126 set up a table of materials for the building and record the specified properties of these materials. The densities and costs are given per square foot of surface. Note that in line 125, ROOF is used to represent a composite construction but is otherwise treated like any other material.

With a table of materials for this building stored in the computer, the designer can now inform the computer of his selection of materials for each surface in the building (lines 127 to 168) (see Fig. 9.9). The OPEN material (line 126) will not contribute to any takeoffs of weight or cost since it has been defined with a cost of 0 and a density of 0. D and C are abbreviated forms for density and cost, respectively.

Line 169 requests calculation of the weight of the concrete wall at the west of the display area RM 101. The final command in the example (line 170) illustrates the ability of the BUILD user to interrogate the computer selectively about the current state of the design. In this case, a list of the spaces containing the activity OFFICE is requested. The computer output has the form shown in Fig. 9.10.

9.5 From Research to Practice

The example of the preceding section indicates the capabilities of the initial version of BUILD. Its limitations and restrictions should be apparent to the reader. Even a greatly simplified description of a limited number of aspects of a relatively simple building has required many pages of BUILD commands. This amount of information is partly inherent in the problem, illustrating once again the magnitude of the amount of data with which the architect deals. It is also partly the result of the BUILD research goals and priorities. Some of the effort that might have gone to make the input language more concise and more convenient to the user was devoted instead to aspects of the system which the user never sees, such as the organization of the information within the computer. In addition, it seemed more important to add new commands to extend the scope of BUILD than to refine the external form of the commands themselves. Some of the awkwardness arises from a desire to be explicit about the design information and the relationships involved. One of the reasons for this deliberate explicitness has been described elsewhere.[28]

> The mention of a computer-based information system for design may suggest a massive library containing all the conceivable data relevant to any building problem. Such a system probably has its place and should be valuable to a discriminating designer, once the technological and economic obstacles to its development have been overcome. In the current research we are trying to identify and work with a minimum base of relevant information and find the discipline of this concept the source of useful insights. This approach implies that the user of BUILD will explicitly specify the data and relationships he feels to be important for his particular problem, using the conventions of the language to reduce the amount of input required for such explicitness.

The transition of BUILD or its successors from research to practice requires more of these input-saving conventions. In establishing these conventions, however, care must be taken to avoid disastrous ambiguities in prescribing the operations that the computer is to perform.

Another need is to extend the modes of interaction between the designer and the computer beyond the written verbal input and output used by the earliest version of BUILD. The first abilities to communicate with BUILD graphically using the display oscilloscope and light pen have been provided by Sommerfeld.[25]

Considerable addition to the scope of BUILD is also essential. At present the problem-oriented languages in ICES that are most directly and immediately useful for building problems are STRUDL for structural analysis and design,[16] COGO for applications to site surveys and geometry,[19] and SEPOL for soils-engineering analyses.[24] At least six other building systems identified in the systems-analysis study need similar integrated languages for their own description, analysis, and evaluation.

Attention also must be given to statements of performance standards and design criteria for use in evaluation. Many of these arise from the requirements of a particular client, building type, or site. Others derive from building codes and zoning regulations. If the current trend toward greater reliance on performance standards continues, and if they come to occupy a more prominent position in building codes and regulations, the value of the computer as a means of predicting and evaluating building performance without the necessity of physically constructing and testing buildings or assemblies of materials will be further enhanced.[33] A theoretical and experimental basis for such an approach is, however, largely lacking.

One of the principal justifications for the effort necessary to maintain a current description of a building in a computer throughout the design process is the ability to use the computer as a means of communication among all those concerned with design decisions. It becomes worthwhile to enter and update large amounts of data because a single item of information can be entered or revised by one member of a design team and be accessible to all the other team members. Some of the related problems of computer system design and programming are beginning to become evident and the objects of research.

Taken together, the kinds of extensions required for a system like BUILD to be useful in practice suggest that there is a minimum capability necessary for widespread adoption in architectural offices. This too will require some experience to determine. The specification of a minimum useful information system for building design is affected greatly by economic factors. If the trend toward more information-processing capability per dollar continues, what the architect can afford will also change. It is the task of research to establish a theoretical framework for computer applications in architecture and to embody the theory in appropriate techniques of computer usage. Without this basis, advances in computing machinery must remain ineffectual for the architect.

Obviously research can flourish only with the encouragement and support of the practicing design professional. Initial efforts such as BUILD can help inform the architect about the kind of design aids that can contribute to his future capabilities. Even these preliminary efforts may be useful in architectural education.[35] In any case they hint at changes in methods and techniques of practice. It should be clear to environmental designers that a new design environment will have far-reaching consequences.

Speculation about these consequences touches the traditions and values, the hopes and fears, of architects, as well as their modes of thought and practice. The use of computers neither guarantees nor precludes the quality of the buildings they may assist an architect to design. In this respect the computer is no more culpable than the triangle and parallel rule or the yellow tracing paper and soft pencil. Imaginative and resourceful architects are likely to find that comprehensive information systems can increase their ability to understand and deal with complex problems and to become aware of the mutual implications of design decisions throughout the design process. Such systems are likely to require even greater attention by the architect to the nonquantifiable factors and human ideals which have been the principal legacy of his professional heritage and the particular pride of his professional service.

REFERENCES

1. C. Alexander, *Notes on the Synthesis of Form,* Harvard University Press, Cambridge, Mass., 1964.
2. S. O. Anderson, quoted in AIA-ACSA Teacher's Seminar, *AIA Journal,* vol. 47, no. 6, p. 77, June, 1967.
3. W. E. Clark and J. J. Souder, "Planning Buildings by Computer," *Architectural and Engineering News,* vol. 7, no. 3, pp. 25–33, March, 1965.
4. S. A. Coons, "The Use of Computers in Technology," *Scientific American,* vol. 215, no. 3, pp. 177–188, September, 1966.
5. P. A. Crisman (ed.), *The Compatible Time-sharing System: A Programmer's Guide,* The M.I.T. Press, Cambridge, Mass., 1965.
6. A. G. H. Dietz, S. L. Danielson, L. C. Teague, Jr., and A. M. Hershdorfer, "Systems Analysis in Building Design," *Proceedings—AIA Architect-Researcher's Conference 1966,* pp. 61–73, Washington University, St. Louis, Mo., Oct. 20–21, 1966, American Institute of Architects, Washington, D.C., March, 1967.
7. G. R. Fair, A. D. J. Flowerdew, W. G. Munro, and D. Rowley, "Note on the Computer as an Aid to the Architect," *The Computer Journal,* vol. 9, no. 1, pp. 16–20, May, 1966.
8. R. M. Fano and F. J. Corbató, "Time-sharing on Computers," *Scientific American,* vol. 215, no. 3, pp. 129–140, September, 1966.
9. S. J. Fenves, "STRESS (Structural Engineering Systems Solver), A Computer Programming System for Structural Engineering Problems," *Technical Report* T63-2, M.I.T. Department of Civil Engineering, May, 1963.
10. S. J. Fenves, R. D. Logcher, S. P. Mauch, and K. F. Reinschmidt, *STRESS: A User's Manual,* The M.I.T. Press, Cambridge, Mass., 1965.
11. D. S. Haviland, *The Computer and the Architectural Profession,* Center for Architectural Research, Rensselaer Polytechnic Institute, Troy, N.Y., 1966.
12. A. M. Hershdorfer, *Understanding the Architectural Design Process through an Analysis of Its Information Structure,* paper presented at the Conference on Computers in Architecture, sponsored by the Computer Education Center of Pratt Institute and the New York Chapter of the American Institute of Architects, United Engineering Center, New York, N.Y., May 23, 1966.
13. A. M. Hershdorfer, *Design-Analysis Systems,* paper presented at the Fourth Conference on Engineering Design and Design Education, Dartmouth College, Hanover, N.H., July 17–18, 1967.

14. T. E. Johnson, "Sketchpad III: A Computer Program for Drawing in Three Dimensions," *American Federation for Information Processing Societies Conference Proceedings*, vol. 23, 1963, pp. 347–353, Spring Joint Computer Conference, Detroit, May, 1963, Spartan Books, New York, N.Y., 1963.

15. S. B. Lipner, "List Processing System for Engineering Application," thesis submitted in partial fulfillment of the requirements for the degree of Master of Science, M.I.T. Department of Civil Engineering, Cambridge, Mass., June, 1966.

16. R. D. Logcher and G. M. Sturman, "STRUDL—A Computer System for Structural Design," *Journal of the Structural Division, Proceedings of the American Society of Civil Engineers*, vol. 92, no. ST6, pp. 191–211, Proceedings Paper 5010, December, 1966.

17. C. L. Miller, *COGO—A Computer Programming System for Civil Engineering Problems*, M.I.T. Department of Civil Engineering, Cambridge, Mass., August, 1961.

18. C. L. Miller, "Man-Machine Communications in Civil Engineering," *Journal of the Structural Division, Proceedings of the American Society of Civil Engineers*, vol. 89, no. ST4, pp. 9ff. August, 1964.

19. C. L. Miller, "General Description of ICES COGO I," Civil Engineering Systems Laboratory, *Research Report* R66-36, M.I.T. Department of Civil Engineering, Cambridge, Mass., July 5, 1966.

20. L. Moseley, "A Rational Design Theory for Planning Buildings Based on the Analysis and Solution of Circulation Problems," *The Architects' Journal*, vol. 138, no. 10, pp. 525–537, Sept. 11, 1963.

21. W. M. Newman, "An Experimental Program for Architectural Design," *The Computer Journal*, vol. 9, no. 1, pp. 21–26, May, 1966.

22. D. Roos and C. L. Miller, "COGO 90: Engineering User's Manual," *Research Report* R64-12, M.I.T. Department of Civil Engineering, Cambridge, Mass., April, 1964.

23. D. Roos, *ICES System Design*, The M.I.T. Press, Cambridge, Mass., 1966.

24. R. L. Schiffman and R. V. Whitman, "ICES-SEPOL I—A Settlement Problem Oriented Language—Systems Design," *Technical Report* T66-3, M.I.T. Department of Civil Engineering, Cambridge, Mass., January, 1966.

25. W. F. Sommerfeld, "A Graphical Information System for Use in Building Design," thesis submitted in partial fulfillment of the requirements for the degree of Master of Science, June, 1967, *Research Report* R67-21, M.I.T. Department of Civil Engineering, Cambridge, Mass., June, 1967.

26. J. J. Souder, W. E. Clark, J. J. Elkind, and M. B. Brown, *Planning for Hospitals: A Systems Approach Using Computer-aided Techniques*, American Hospital Association, Chicago, Ill., 1964.

27. I. E. Sutherland, "A Man-Machine Graphical Communication System," *American Federation for Information Processing Societies Conference Proceedings*, vol. 23, 1963, pp. 329–346, Spring Joint Computer Conference, Detroit, May, 1963, Spartan Books, New York, N.Y., 1963.

28. L. C. Teague, Jr., and A. M. Hershdorfer, *BUILD—An Integrated System for Building Design*, paper presented at the ASCE Structural Engineering Conference, Seattle, Wash., May 8–12, 1967, Conference Preprint 500, American Society of Civil Engineers, New York, N.Y.

29. L. C. Teague, Jr., B. L. Gerken, and W. F. Sommerfeld, *A User's Guide to BUILD*, M.I.T. Department of Civil Engineering, Cambridge, Mass., June, 1967.

30. B. Whitehead and M. Z. Eldars, "An Approach to the Optimum Layout of Single-storey Buildings," *The Architects' Journal*, vol. 139, no. 25, pp. 1373–1380, June 17, 1964.

31. "Architecture and the Computer," *Proceedings of the First Boston Architectural Center Conference,* Dec. 5, 1964, Boston Architectural Center, Boston, Mass.

32. "Computers in Building: Planning Accommodations for Hospitals and the Transportation Problem Technique," *The Architects' Journal,* vol. 138, no. 3, pp. 139–142, July 17, 1963.

33. *Computer-aided Checking of Design Documents for Compliance with Regulatory Codes,* Bolt, Beranek and Newman, Inc., Cambridge, Mass., July, 1965.

34. *Development of Notation and Data Structure for Computer Applications to Building Problems,* Bolt, Beranek and Newman, Inc., Cambridge, Mass., March, 1967.

35. *The Computer—Its Current Role in Architectural Education,* Association of Collegiate Schools of Architecture, Washington, D.C., 1967.

CHAPTER TEN *Coming Attractions*

By G. Neil Harper

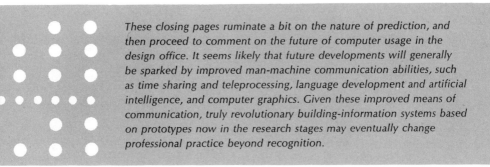

These closing pages ruminate a bit on the nature of prediction, and then proceed to comment on the future of computer usage in the design office. It seems likely that future developments will generally be sparked by improved man-machine communication abilities, such as time sharing and teleprocessing, language development and artificial intelligence, and computer graphics. Given these improved means of communication, truly revolutionary building-information systems based on prototypes now in the research stages may eventually change professional practice beyond recognition.

10.1 Preliminary Remarks on Prediction

The art of predicting the future has fascinated man throughout the ages. The very earliest days of civilization had astrologers and soothsayers whose main stock in trade was predicting future events. Biblical times had dream interpreters, prophets, and wise men. Palm readers, tea-leaves interpreters, and crystal-ball gypsies have all profited by this human desire to forecast the future. More modern times have seen the emergence of a variety of prognosticators who try to establish a link with the future: public-opinion researchers, securities analysts, economic and political forecasters, and a developing breed of the so-called "futurists" whose main function is to invent, project, extrapolate, imagine, and/or guess what the future has in store.

The point of the remarks above is to indicate that this closing chapter stands in a line of well-honored tradition. Though modern analytical techniques have lent an aura of respectability and a tinge of the scientific method to current attempts to predict the future, the basically unknown nature of the future is almost certain to bring even the most sophisticated, the least risky, the most conservative prediction to occasional dishonor. The current chapter, of course, is no exception to the inexorable ground rules of prediction—that each and every body of predictions will occasionally miss the mark by greater or lesser extent.

The main difficulty in accurate forecasting of technological development over any period of time is that it is simply impossible to foresee the sudden, impulsive breakthroughs that characterize scientific discovery and that have such decisive influence on the course of technological development. Hence the task of prediction of technology is somewhat akin to predicting the flow of a river in a region prone to earthquakes. As long as no major breakthroughs in the earth's crust occur, the future flow of the river can be extrapolated from the past with some measure of accuracy. As soon as a major eruption occurs, all predictions may become completely invalid. And unfortunately, major technological breakthroughs, like earthquakes, defy prediction.

Fortunately, the probability of a random disturbance (technological breakthrough) occurring in any given time period decreases as that time period grows shorter. In other words, if a prediction based upon extrapolation of the past is confined to the short-term future, there is a relatively good chance that it may have some measure of accuracy. This chapter of prediction is based on that premise.

There are at least four streams of major activity that seem likely to have significant influence in shaping the course of future computer applications in architecture and engineering: time sharing, language development, computer graphics, and building-systems design. The common thread which pervades each of these topics is one of communication; each presents a different facet of the general problem of allowing the designer to develop and transmit his design concepts and requirements from man to machine and from machine to man. So in a very real sense, the future developments in computer applications will be connected with improved methods for man-machine communication.

It is in this light of improved man-machine communication that future developments should be viewed. Man has thus far been without parallel in his abilities for heuristics, synthesis, imagination, inventiveness. The machine is a proved master for speed in directed computation, logic, and analysis. Hence a union of the best of man's abilities with the best of the machine's capacities promises to bear rewards of unprecedented usefulness and value.

10.2   Time Sharing and Teleprocessing

One of the problems in the past which has impeded the development of computer applications has been the difficulty for small and medium-sized offices to have access to a computer. Although developments in transistors, mass-production techniques, and general know-how have made it possible for many offices to lease small computers, some of the more exciting developments in the future will be applications requiring the services of large computers in small amounts of time. Hence the concept of time sharing has a definite appeal for certain types of applications.

Time sharing is, as the name implies, the sharing of time of a single large computer by a number of users. Typically the user has at his disposal a small typewriter-like terminal, which in some instances is equipped with card-reading and punching devices, and which is connected to a large central computer. Such time-shared systems have been able to accommodate anywhere from a half dozen to as many as a hundred or so such terminals operating at the same time.

Under optimum conditions, it appears to the individual user that he is the only user of the large computer. In reality, the monitoring system for the large machine is slicing the time continuum into very small increments of time, of the order of a hundredth or a thousandth of a second, and giving one such increment of time to each user in the current cycle of active terminals. If user A's problem is not finished in this small increment of time on the first cycle through the active terminals, he receives another burst of time on the second pass around the circle, etc. Such a mode of computer usage is obviously best suited for those kinds of problems which require a high degree of man-machine interaction and where each of the commands which the man issues can be accomplished in small amounts of time and the answer printed back for man's consideration before the next command is issued.

Although many problems in architecture and engineering are ideally suited to this type of approach, certain classes of problems require relatively large amounts of computer time in order to arrive at a solution. This consideration, when coupled with the observation that there is an inherent overhead cost in pure time-shared systems (in terms of switching one user's program to and from memory numerous times before his program is executed to completion), has led to modified versions of time-shared systems whereby there are certain "foreground" and "background" activities. For those classes of the user's commands which are recognized as implying very brief computer time in order to execute to completion, the system operates in a fashion similar to that described above. This is the so-called "foreground" activity. The commands which imply relatively long processing times are kept queued up in the background and are brought forward only at specified times or at times when there is no call for foreground activity. This appears to be a more efficient use of the machine and should result in better overall service to the user.

An obvious addition to time-shared systems which should make them even more efficient and attractive is that of a small-sized computer for use as an input-output terminal, rather than the simple typewriter-like console described above. Many problems could be partly solved, or preprocessed, at the small local computer station, and then transmitted to the larger central machine only when large-scale power was required. The results could be returned to the small computer for postprocessing and output. A very limited number of such small computer input-output stations have already been placed in operation, and results are thus far quite encouraging. As one prime example, it now appears that computer graphics may head in this direction with a small computer used as an interface between the designer at the console and the large computer in the background.

An activity frequently associated with time sharing is teleprocessing. The connection of a terminal or small computer to the large central computer is normally done by means of existing telephone lines. The actual transmission of data over the lines is the activity called teleprocessing. This transmitting can be over private lines which connect two or more points without entering a telephone exchange or over regular lines which are transmitted over the great complex of national and international telephone networks. Work is also proceeding on the use of satellites for transmission of computer information from point to point.

Various transmission rates exist for various grades of usage. Rates of transmission are normally quoted in bits (a binary digit with only two possible states, say 0 and 1, on or off, etc.) per second or words per minute. Figure 10.1 shows typical available transmission rates. Also shown in the figure are the transmission rates converted from bits per second to the more comprehensible words or pages of information per minute. The standard eight bits per character, six characters per word, sixty characters per line, and fifty lines per page have been used in these conversions.

	Bits/second	Words/minute	Pages/minute
Low-Grade (Narrow bandwidth)	50	60	1/8
Voice-grade (Intermediate bandwidth)	2,000	2,400	5
High-grade (Broad bandwidth)	500,000	600,000	1250

Fig. 10.1   Transmission rates for teleprocessing

For some offices, the use of time sharing and teleprocessing appears to offer many attractions. It should be pointed out, however, that these systems are still very new and that many issues are yet to be resolved before unqualified endorsement of this mode of usage is given. Even if the complete computer hardware and transmission questions were resolved, at the moment relatively few appropriate computer programs are available for profitable professional use of the systems. The demarcations regarding proper division of the work load to local service bureaus on a batch-process basis, to smaller in-house computers, or to the large, time-shared computer are by no means clear. And there are a whole range of questions in the social, legal, and economic implications of large-scale public-utility networks of computers servicing the nation. In summary, while the prospects and promises of some sort of time sharing look very bright indeed, we are just at the beginning of an era of explosive developments which eventually will require workable solutions to the types of questions posed above.

10.3   Language Development and Artificial Intelligence

The concepts of language and intelligence are in some way inextricably bound together. Intelligence could be variously defined as the ability to reason, to learn, to understand. Language could be defined as a mechanism for communicating. Intelligence alone seems somehow to be incomplete or insufficient without a method of communicating that intelligence. Likewise, the concept of language as a type of communication ability seems also to be incomplete without some subject matter or intelligence stream to transmit.

The term "artificial" intelligence has been used to describe the exhibition, by a computer, of the ability to "learn" from past experience. Although a comprehensive discussion of this field is beyond the scope of this book,* a narrowly delineated portion of the field dealing with language development has been selected for discussion. In particular, what will be discussed here is the increasing capacity of modern computers for "understanding" types of language which have heretofore been reserved as the province of humans. Strictly speaking, these language capabilities do not fit the narrower definitions of artificial intelligence, since most of the language-translation programs to date have little if any ability to modify themselves, or "learn," from past experience. However, a broader notion of the meaning of intelligence in terms of the capacity to interpret and understand a stream of information is pertinent to the following discussion.

The flurry of current activity in the construction of language translators is almost certain to have a significant influence on the forms of future applications in architectural and engineering practice. The reader has already been introduced to some of these new forms of languages in terms of the problem-oriented languages discussed in several of the earlier chapters. Even beyond these particular languages, however, is the level of sophistication in language development which makes it possible to construct problem-oriented languages for generating other problem-oriented languages.

A little reflection should indicate what a remarkable and significant accomplishment this really is. With such a tool available, it is possible, even for an intermediate-level programmer, to construct a language which is immediately interpretable by the machine. And the construction of the language itself is done within the environment of a special problem-oriented language. As a matter of fact, the COGO, STRUDL, PROJECT, and BUILD languages discussed in earlier chapters were all constructed using

---

* The reader is referred, for example, to the works of Wiener, Minsky, etc., for the more general definitions of this field. An excellent introduction to some of the concepts and recent developments in artificial intelligence is contained in the September, 1966, issue of the *Scientific American*.

a single problem-oriented language, the so-called Command Definition Language (CDL).*

Figure 10.2 presents a partial list of commands from this CDL. Commands such as those listed in Fig. 9.2 would be used to construct other commands for a user-defined problem-oriented language. No attempt is

```
ADD
REPLACE
MODIFIER
CONDITION
REPEAT
IGNORE
FILE
```

Fig. 10.2   Selected commands from the command-definition language

made to instruct the reader in the actual use of this Command Definition Language. The intent here is to indicate the general nature of the commands which a user would have available to construct another language. Whether the language so produced is in English, French, German, Russian, or any other stream of intelligible symbols is immaterial to the Command Definition Language. Likewise, the actual professional field of application is unimportant—applications could be in architectural planning, financial analysis, mechanical engineering, acoustics, traffic patterns, etc. A list of imaginary commands from several disciplines which might make sense and which could easily be defined and used with the Command Definition Language is given in Fig. 10.3.

```
DETERMINE DISTANCE FROM ROOM 'B1' TO ROOM '2211'
COMPUTE SQ FT IN ZONE 3
TABULATE WINDOW WALL COSTS
COMPARE HEAT GAINS AT TIME 1030 AND TIME 1200
CHECK WIND DRIFT AT FLOOR 30
ESTIMATE POWER CONSUMPTION FOR SCHEME 'A'
```

Fig. 10.3   Imaginary commands definable by the command-definition language

It should be emphasized that the particular commands listed in Fig. 10.3 are completely imaginary but that the capacity to produce such commands is quite real. Hence the situation in regard to this kind of artificial intel-

---

* The Command Definition Language was developed primarily by Ron Walter and his associates in the M.I.T. Department of Civil Engineering, under the ICES project. For further study, the interested reader is referred to *ICES: Programmer's Reference Manual*, M.I.T. Department of Civil Engineering, Cambridge, Mass., October, 1967.

ligence in language development is similar in some respects to the situation in time sharing. In both fields, the course and utility of future developments will be very much a function of the imagination and industry of the man using the system. The impact which well-constructed languages can have on the practicing professional should be clearly evident.

10.4   Computer Graphics

Computer graphics is a topic of considerable fascination for many architects and engineers. That this is a topic of natural interest is not surprising, since a good portion of the output from a professional design office is graphical in one form or another. A very brief survey of some of the developments in computer graphics is offered in the paragraphs that follow.

Experimental applications of computer graphics in architectural practice tend to cluster around three main types of hardware units available for displaying results. Though perhaps not normally thought of as a graphic tool, the familiar line printer has proved abilities for certain kinds of relatively coarse applications. A more conventional graphical-output device is the XY plotter. Relatively complex detail drawings of machine parts have been produced with these instruments, though graphs and contour plotting are more typical of actual office applications. Perhaps most versatile and promising of the output units now available is the cathode-ray tube, or "scope." Fascinating displays of wire-figure diagrams of bridges, electric circuits, building elevations, and perspectives and a host of others have been made for demonstration purposes.

It is beginning to appear that the most likely path of future developments in computer graphics for architectural and engineering practice will be done on computer-driven oscilloscopes rather than on line printers or plotters. It is not at all difficult to think of what one would like to be able to do with such hardware. One of the first practical applications that comes to mind would involve the generation, retrieval, modification, and printing of standard details. What one might like to be able to do in the office of the future, for example, would be to generate standard details at the oscilloscope and to file them away in digitalized form on disk or tape. Later one could recall a series of particular details for viewing and possible modification, and then give an instruction like "print detail number 6 in location B-2 on sheet S-16." When all the desired selections from available office standards had been so chosen and positioned, a beginning set of working drawings could be displayed on the oscilloscope, a film made, and the set printed on linen for continued development by a draftsman.

This kind of computerized graphical ability has direct implications for both the design office and educational institutions. Graphical recall ability could make it possible to transmit detail design experience to the student or young professional in a very short amount of time. Hence certain types of experience which now comes only after several years of practice could be much more readily attained—perhaps even before leaving the educational environment.

There are, of course, more advanced types of applications of computer graphics than those described above.* The practical application of the techniques involved generally is linked, either knowingly or unknowingly, with development of comprehensive building-information systems. In this sense, computer graphics assumes its role as a mechanism for input-output to a systematized storage of building data within computer memory.

This summary of computer graphics is not particularly insightful nor is it necessarily comprehensive. But perhaps it does give some notion of the kinds of applications which are under study and development. In the discussions of time sharing and language development, it was fairly evident that there would be almost immediate practical applications whose use would extend for some time into the future. Unfortunately, the case is not so clear for computer graphics. Despite the truly remarkable advances which are being made in some isolated experimental developments, the immediate future of computer graphics for office practice is clouded considerably by both technical and economic difficulties.

10.5 Building-information Systems

Perhaps one of the most important areas of research in computer applications is in the area of building-information systems. In fact, most of the topics discussed in earlier chapters—STRUDL for structural engineering, PROJECT for networking, BUILD for space and surface location, and programs for accounting, specifications, and estimating—can all be thought of as activities belonging to a single, comprehensive building-information system.

It seems quite likely that the kinds of information that will be put into the large-scale storage systems of the future will be very much the same kinds of information that now are being used in the various facets of the overall design and construction process. In a fanciful system of the future,

---

* A number of excellent films on computer graphics showing some basic abilities in computerized sketches, automotive design, animated-cartoon production, simulated aircraft landings, changing architectural perspectives, etc., have been produced on an experimental basis by a variety of large-scale computer groups. None of these applications has been directly usable in the professional office, however.

for example, the architectural designer might describe the overall building geometry by sketching elevations and floor plans—again with the light pen, and at the architectural console. This information becomes a part of the building data system and is therefore available immediately at the structural-engineering console where it can be used for the structural frame analysis. The architect, of course, continues to add information to the system through his console by selecting materials for walls and roof, partitioning floors into rooms, developing sections and details, etc.

With the geometry and material selection available at the mechanical-engineering console, heat gain and loss computations can be made, and environmental systems designed. Checks can be made by the mechanical engineer against the information being provided to the system by the structural engineer to assure compatibility of geometry for air-conditioning ducts versus structural members. Periodically, readings could be taken from this developing data base to provide cost information for estimating and budget-comparison purposes.

As this building data system nears completion, it is not completely unreasonable to suggest that a magnetic tape or a disk bearing this information, rather than the familiar working drawings and specifications, now becomes the primary instrument of communication between designer and contractor. Instead of sending out sets of drawings and specifications, the design office now sends out a magnetic tape with equivalent information on it. The steel fabricator could drive automatic cutting and welding equipment directly from the tape; the concrete-reinforcing-bar shop could cut, bend, bundle, and ship the rebars with automatic equipment driven by the tape; and the contractor might have numerically controlled erection equipment, also driven by the same building-system-information tape. In short, graphical and textual information (which could of course be reproduced from this same building-systems tape) would be required only for communication from man to man. The primary communication in the future may well be from the designers' computers to the contractors' computers.

Whenever one begins to link this kind of fantasy to existing capabilities, it is inevitable that he will very early discover some major obstacles that lie in the way of the realization of his fantasy. From a practical point of view, an enormous amount of detail is contained in even a modest set of working drawings. This staggering detail, when coupled with the complex computer storage requirements for even the simplest graphical display, is a difficulty that is not likely to be easily solved in the near future. In short, man's age-old talent for drawing—whether on linen or the walls of a cave— is a remarkably efficient mode of communication, at least for human beings.

A second formidable obstacle to early widespread use of building-data systems such as that described above is that we are nowhere near developing the comprehensive systems software (computer programs) for handling this massive data. The nature and classification of the data itself are still a subject of much discussion and research. Preliminary work that is being done in this area not only indicates the extreme crudeness of existing building-systems software but also casts a shadow of doubt on the capabilities of existing computer hardware to store and process the data.

A third major difficulty to be overcome is that of economics. Graphical input-output units are at the moment far beyond the range of even the largest professional offices. And for truly creative exploitation of graphics, these devices demand large-scale computing power. Though it seems likely that small special- and general-purpose computers can be used as interfaces between the graphical units and the large computer, it also seems likely that full use of sophisticated computer graphics must await the development of economical time-sharing systems—and here again we are only at the beginning of an era.

Even given sufficient financial support, there remains the problem of expert personnel. Although our universities are beginning to train young professionals in computer techniques, it takes several years of intensive work in the area to attain a respectable mastery of even a relatively small part of computer applications. Furthermore, it is becoming increasingly clear that people highly trained in computer sciences as a rule have limited backgrounds in actual architectural or engineering disciplines. And unfortunately the converse is also true—that talented engineers and architects have normally had little time to devote to becoming proficient in computer techniques. Hence the problem of personnel is likely to remain critical and will be solved only by extending the education and experience of both the computer specialist and the practicing professional.

Such a comprehensive building-information system as described above is, admittedly, fanciful. But the need for better-integrated systems that make common data readily available to a wide variety of designers, engineers, estimators, and fabricators has always been quite real. Hence any development in the systematic integration of the common data needed by various disciplines will undoubtedly have an important effect on the overall practice of those engaged in the building-construction industry.

10.6 Conclusion

Most of the developments discussed in this chapter have already been proved to be technically feasible. The all-too-frequent error in prediction of the future, however, lies in confusing what is technically feasible with what is practically expedient and economically sound. By and large, the emphasis in this chapter—as indeed in the whole book—has been more on topics which seem to offer promise of practical utility. As mentioned earlier, prophecy for long-term development, like mathematical extrapolation, becomes increasingly error-prone the farther one projects. It is quite clear, however, that the obstacles to be overcome in the optimistic long-term projections are by no means insignificant. But by the same token, a reasonable expenditure of effort to attain these worthwhile goals may well be the mark of vitality and growth potential for the professional office of the future.

Index

Index